NATIONAL COLLEGE OF EDUCATION

TEST OF ADOLESCENT/ADULT
WORD FINDING   TAWF

Diane J. German, Ph.D.

TECHNICAL MANUAL

DLM
Teaching
Resources

Designed by Plunk Design

ISBN   1-55924-289-2

0 9 8 7 6 5 4 3 2 1 90 91 92 93 94 95 96 97 98

The TAWF is dedicated to my father, my cousin, and my husband, Arthur.

Thank you, for it is together that we make this contribution to adolescents and adults everywhere in the hopes that it will help them in their efforts to improve their expressive language skills.

TABLE OF CONTENTS

LIST OF TABLES

LIST OF FIGURES

ABOUT THE TEST AUTHOR

Dr. Diane German is a professor in the department of Special Education in the National College of Education at National-Louis University in Evanston, Illinois. She has been a professor in special education teacher training programs for 18 years. First she was Director of the Learning Disabilities Teacher Training Program and Diagnostic and Remedial Clinic for children with language and learning disorders at the College of Racine in Racine, Wisconsin, and then Director of the certification program in learning disabilities at the University of Wisconsin-Parkside in Kenosha, Wisconsin. Prior to her work at the university, she was a speech and language pathologist in Wilmette Public Schools, District #39, Wilmette, Illinois. Dr. German received her B.S. degree in speech and language pathology at Indiana University, Bloomington, Indiana, and her M.A. and Ph.D. in Language and Learning Disabilities from Northwestern University, Evanston, Illinois. She has published extensively in the area of word-finding disorders in children and has presented numerous workshops, miniseminars, technical papers, and short courses at state and national conferences on the Diagnosis of and Intervention for Word-Finding Disorders in Children. Dr. German is the author of the *Test of Word Finding* (TWF).

ACKNOWLEDGMENTS

As author of the National College of Education *Test of Adolescent/Adult Word Finding* (TAWF), I feel extremely fortunate in having had many fine professionals participate in its development. Constructing the TAWF, conducting the national standardization, and preparing the TAWF for publication was a comprehensive, multifaceted endeavor that could not have been accomplished without the efforts of many people providing support at each phase of test development. It is with great gratitude and appreciation that I acknowledge the contributions of these professionals.

DLM is the ideal publisher for the TAWF. I thank their fine staff, beginning with the president, Andrew Bingham, for his excellent leadership and his continual commitment to the development of quality materials in the area of word-finding disorders. I thank the project editors, Dr. Judy Werder, for her leadership during the standardization phase; Tom Hutchinson, for sharing his editorial expertise and sensitivity to field needs in the final preparation of the TAWF manuals; Gloria Starr, for her very thorough approach to coordinating the TAWF *Test Book;* and the coordinator of the TAWF standardization, Holly Witt, for her endurance and tenacity. The contributions of other DLM staff members, John Starkel and Linda Ross, were also greatly appreciated throughout the production of the TAWF.

I feel most fortunate to have had Dr. Doris Kistler, University of Wisconsin–Madison, serve as my technical consultant and statistician for the TAWF. I thank her for her rigorous, thorough approach to test development, her commitment to excellence, and her willingness to share her extensive knowledge base in the development of the TAWF. A special thank you goes to several professionals who helped in the raw data preparation: Marianne Arruda, Dave D'Angelo, Terry D'Angelo, Margot Gillin, Mary Haggerty, Katherine V. Nelson, Carol Noland, and Jim Walker.

I also wish to thank John Steiger of Riverwoods, Illinois, the TAWF artist, for his superb artwork in the TAWF, and Dr. Bonnie Litowitz for her insightful and helpful comments on the TAWF manuals.

Numerous professionals participated in the standardization program of the TAWF. Many administrators, in support of the TAWF, coordinated the data collection process in their individual school districts. I thank them for their steadfast support before and while the TAWF standardization team was in their individual school districts. Actual data for the standardization of the TAWF was collected by speech and language pathologists, learning disability professionals, and students in training in these professions and in school psychology. I feel fortunate to have had such a well-qualified data collection team. I am grateful to the following professionals who participated in the standardization program for the TAWF: *Local Coordinators:* Bonnie Taylor, M.S., CCC-A, in Scottsdale, Arizona; Nancy Crosby, M.A., CCC-SP, in Oakland, California; Carol Nolan, M.A., CCC-SP, in Palatine, Illinois; Ann Fuller in Litchfield, Minnesota; Donna Hamm in Boston, Massachusetts; Pam Brewer, Jennie Boger, and Boyd Nash in Albemarle and Norwood, North Carolina; Beth Voltz in Pittsburgh, Pennsylvania; Rebecca Molidor, M.S., CCC-SP, in Lake Dallas, Lewisville, and Coppell, Texas; and Katherine V. Nelson, M.S., CCC-SP, in Racine, Wisconsin; *TAWF Testers:* Judith L. Shanahan, Penny S. Martin, Molly D. Mudick, Verna J. Zabramski, and Mary Permoda in Arizona; Libby Eoff in Arkansas; Robert Blades, Delores Godbold, and Carol Henderson in California; Lori Markin in Colorado; Beth Muller in Connecticut; Judy Katz in Florida; Judy Brault, Marlene Douglas, Terry D'Angelo, Glenna House, Pamela A. Jessee, Anne Werhane, Debbie Myers, Phyllis Duffie, Jown C. Notter, Lisa Isenstein, A.G. Isaacs, Margilee Jacobs, and Richard Swastek in Illinois; Rebecca Riddle in Indiana; Linda Tucker, Terry Rodriquez, Debbie Cihen, Wendy Levin, Sherri Miller, and Betsy Posnick in Massachusetts; Cecelia C. Landau in Michigan; JoAnne Gabrielson, Jolene Jorgenson, and Sue Decker in Minnesota; Lisa Stacy in Missouri; Carole Hitchison in New Jersey; Jane Kerr, Annette Widelski, Millie Snodgrass, Diane Hatley, Elene Morgan, and Clarene Coley in North Carolina; Odette Maimbourg in Ohio; Sandra Smith, Judith Aloi, Nancy Howell, and Linda Blutas in Pennsylvania; Steve Belanger and Alan Gravell in Rhode Island; Sally Powers, Jolene Seabourn, Debbie Krafchek, Sandra Smith, Kathleen Thomas, Sandy Denton, Tracy Warren, Karin Glenn, Karen Kennedy, Jerilyn Totty, Carrie Kerr, Gail Liebensberger, Jill Apple, and Maria Wilson in Texas; T. J. Healy and Connie Kuhrt in Washington; Janet Anderson, Lynn Stewart, Ella

Hearn, Joyce Braid, Mary Eschmann, Alberat Nielsen, Mary Ann Toutant, Monica Dombeck, Linda T. Christ, and Lisa Canadeo in Wisconsin.

I was fortunate to have excellent administrators, schools, and centers participating in the TAWF standardization program. I am grateful for their participation, their total cooperation, and their commitment to research in the schools. Names of participating centers, schools, and their principals are indicated below.

West

Coronado High School
Scottsdale, Arizona
Dr. Ed Cegrave, Principal

Skyline High School
Oakland, California
James Welsh, Principal

Monera Junior High School
Oakland, California
Richard Adams, Principal

South

Lake Dallas High School
Lake Dallas, Texas
Jim Akard, Principal
Marsha Keffer, Counselor

Lake Dallas Middle School
Lake Dallas, Texas
Mike Pearson, Principal

Coppell High School
Coppell, Texas
Dr. Lu Stephens, Principal

Coppell Middle School
Coppell, Texas
Vern Edin, Principal

Lewisville High School
Lewisville, Texas
Doug Killough, Principal

South Stanly High School
Norwood, North Carolina
George H. Reynolds, Principal

Northeast

Our Lady of Lourdes
Jamaica Plains, Massachusetts
Sister Patricia Andrews, Principal

St. Gregory's High School
Dorchester, Massachusetts
Sister Karen Hokanson, Principal

Mission Church High School
Roxbury, Massachusetts
Sister Frances Butler, Principal

Columbkille High School
Brighton, Massachusetts
Sister Maria Delaney, Principal

Columbkille Junior High School
Brighton, Massachusetts
Mary Battles, Principal

Keystone Oaks High School
Pittsburgh, Pennsylvania
Dr. Peter O'Donnell, Principal
William Spence, Principal

Vanderbilt Rehabilitation Center
Newport, Rhode Island
Nancy Lineberry, Speech and
Language Pathologist
Steven Belanger, Speech and Language
Pathologist
Alan Gravell, Speech and Language
Pathologist

Jeff Neff Middle School
Pittsburgh, Pennsylvania
Gregg Beyer, Principal

North Central

Horlick High School
Racine, Wisconsin
Larry Yarck, Principal

Starbuck Middle School
Racine, Wisconsin
Jetha Pinkston, Principal
Dick Ehlert, Counselor

Washington Park High School
Racine, Wisconsin
Bob Crist, Principal

Gilmore Middle School
Racine, Wisconsin
Ronald Olson, Principal

Wheeling High School
Wheeling, Illinois
Dr. Thomas Shirley, Principal
Tom Hansen, Counselor

Oliver W. Holmes Middle School
Oak Park, Illinois
Avrum Poster, Principal
Wendy Billingham, Assistant Principal

Robert Healy Elementary School
Chicago, Illinois
Beverly Tunney, Principal

University of Michigan Residential
Aphasia Clinic
University of Michigan
Ann Arbor, Michigan

Litchfield High School
Litchfield, Minnesota
John Deir, Principal

Litchfield Junior High School
Litchfield, Minnesota
William Gray, Principal

CHAPTER ONE

PURPOSE AND THEORETICAL PERSPECTIVE OF THE TAWF

GENERAL PURPOSE

Although the presence of word-finding problems in children has long been recognized (Johnson & Myklebust, 1967; Rutherford & Telser, 1967), it has only been in the last 15 years that this expressive language disorder in children has been the focus of research. Recent literature and empirical investigations have centered on the definition, characteristics, prevalence, assessment, and intervention of word-finding problems in children (Denckla & Rudel, 1976a, 1976b; Fried-Oken, 1984; German, 1979, 1983, 1984; Leonard, Nippold, Kail, & Hale, 1983; Wiig & Semel, 1976, 1984; Wiig, Semel, & Nystrom, 1982; Wolf, 1980). Most recently, a nationally standardized test designed to assess word-finding disorders in children of elementary-school age, the *Test of Word Finding* (TWF) (German, [1986] 1989), was published. This instrument was developed because of a strong need in the field for a standardized test, supported by nationally representative, normative data, that would provide professionals with a systematic procedure for assessing children's word-finding skills. To respond to this same need in the diagnosis of word-finding disorders in the adolescent and adult population, the National College of Education *Test of Adolescent/Adult Word Finding* (TAWF) was developed. The TAWF was designed to assist professionals in the assessment of adolescents' and adults' word-finding skills by providing extensively researched naming tasks and systematic test procedures supported by reliability and validity investigations and representative normative data.

SCHOOL AND CLINIC USES

IDENTIFICATION

The TAWF is intended to assist speech and language pathologists, learning disability teachers, school psychologists, reading specialists, and other clinicians and special educators in assessing word-finding skills in adolescents and adults. Prior to the development of the TAWF, professionals often relied on informal assessment to determine word-finding difficulties in adolescents and adults. Although insightful, the results of such assessments often demonstrated poor reliability and were difficult to document and communicate to parents, other family members, and school or medical personnel. In contrast, the TAWF provides the examiner with a formal, reliable assessment procedure for measuring a person's accuracy (standard scores and percentile ranks) and speed (response time) in naming. Because the TAWF allows the examiner to compare an individual's naming performance with that of normal adolescents and adults in a large standardization sample, a person's word-finding skills can be reliably identified. In addition, the TAWF presents procedures for analyzing the nature of naming responses and for observing the presence of secondary characteristics (gestures and extra verbalizations) of naming behavior, resulting in a more precise identification of word-finding difficulties. In summary, the TAWF provides a structure for describing an individual's naming behavior to parents, other family members, teachers, and school or medical personnel with respect to accuracy, speed, substitution types, and the presence of gestures and extra verbalizations.

PROGRAMMING

Intervention for word-finding disorders falls into three categories: remediation, compensatory programming, and self-awareness. Intervention effectiveness is based on the professional's understanding of the individual's word-finding skills. Although word-finding assessment should include information from many sources (diagnostic tests, home and classroom observations, etc.), information obtained from the TAWF enhances one's understanding of a person's word-finding skills and thus aids in determining the most appropriate intervention program for people with word-finding difficulties.

A series of special TAWF features provides valuable programming information. Individuals with both accuracy and response-time difficulties need programming that is different from those manifesting either accuracy or response-time deficits alone. Therefore, comparisons of TAWF response time and accuracy can guide appropriate intervention techniques for a particular person. Second, the TAWF provides a model for analyzing substitution responses expressed by someone who is having difficulty finding a target word. Knowledge of the unique substitutions used by a particular person while manifesting word-finding difficulties can provide insights into the type of naming strategies employed. Thus the substitution analyses on the TAWF yield information important for individualizing remedial programs. Last, the TAWF provides a means of analyzing secondary characteristics of word-finding problems. An analysis of such secondary characteristics that accompany word-finding difficulties is helpful to individuals who must learn to inhibit such behaviors and to parents or other family members and teachers or other school or medical personnel who need to recognize these behaviors to identify when specific individuals manifest difficulties in word finding. This multifaceted approach to the assessment of word-finding skills contributes to the development of a more comprehensive, individualized intervention program for the person with word-finding problems.

REMEDIAL PROGRESS AND PROGRAM EVALUATION

Because of its psychometrically robust and technically sound diagnostic characteristics, the TAWF can also be used in evaluating remedial progress. For example, follow-up testing at specific intervals can provide documentation of progress and help determine if a given remedial program is appropriate.

Specifically, a pre- and posttest assessment sequence allows the examiner to observe improvement in both naming speed and accuracy, as well as changes in naming strategies and reduction of secondary characteristics following a specific period of intervention.

RESEARCH

The TAWF is an effective and appropriate instrument for investigating word-finding skills. Its standardized procedures and normative data allow the researcher to conduct reliable and valid comparative investigations of adolescents' and adults' word-finding skills. Because both the formal and informal evaluations of the TAWF consider variables identified through research as important in word-finding assessment, researchers can conduct comprehensive investigations of their subjects' word-finding abilities.

Research investigating the prevalence and nature of word-finding deficits in various groups of adolescents and studies of the relationship between word-finding skills and academic achievement could be conducted using the TAWF. In particular, the incidence of word-finding difficulties in normal achieving and exceptional populations could be established. Use of the TAWF would enable researchers to compare the word-finding skills of normally language-learning students with those of stutterers, bilingual students, linguistically handicapped students with and without receptive language problems, and other exceptional individuals. The results of such investigations would provide insights into the various manifestations of this expressive language disorder.

TAWF is also appropriate for studying word-retrieval skills in special adult populations such as adult aphasics and adults with neurological disorders, head trauma, and language disorders. Use of the comprehension section in the TAWF will help examiners differentiate receptive versus expressive language problems in these special groups. Further, because normative data are provided for adults 20 to 80 years old, the TAWF would be useful in the study of naming skills in the normal aging population. In addition, use of the TAWF substitution analysis provides a framework for analyzing both adolescents' and adults' semantic-processing skills.

WORD-FINDING PROBLEMS IN ADULT POPULATIONS

Much of our understanding of children's word-finding problems stems from time-honored investigations of the adult neurological disorder, aphasia. Therefore, a logical approach to a discussion of word-finding disorders is to begin with a review of the traditional concepts and classifications of this condition as found in adult aphasia. The following is a brief review of some fundamental properties of adult word-finding problems as presented by major aphasiologists. The works of Broca and Bastian (cited in Cohn, 1970) were among the earliest investigations of naming disorders in adult aphasics. Broca identified "verbal amnesia" as a speech defect resulting from a loss of memory for words (cited in Cohn, 1970), whereas Bastian (Weisenburg & McBride, 1964) described two language disturbances, amnesia and aphasia. Amnesia patients were distinguished by disturbances in word retrieval and thinking, while aphasics were described as those demonstrating speech or writing disturbances. The now-classical concept and definition of amnesic aphasia was introduced by Gelb and Goldstein (cited in Cohn, 1970). They defined amnesic aphasia as a disorder which results in an inability to recall specific names of common things, in turn leading to circumlocutory or functional descriptive speech in place of the implied word. However, Goldstein did not see this naming disorder as stemming primarily from a loss of memory for words but rather as an impairment of the abstract attitude required for accurate naming. Head (1926) suggested the following four categories of aphasia: verbal, syntactical, nominal, and semantic. Among these, the nominal classification most nearly resembles the amnesic aphasic—a patient exhibiting primary problems in word finding.

More recent classifications of aphasia also focus on word-finding disorders. A review of these works indicates that some classifications describe word-finding problems as a symptom of a more general aphasia, whereas others designate this disorder as a clinical entity in itself (Fried-Oken, 1984). For example, Wepman, Bock, Jones, and Van Pelt (1956) derived a model of aphasia in which they grouped aphasic subjects' verbal disorders into five categories: global, jargon, pragmatic, semantic, and syntactic. Word-finding difficulties were included among the semantic disorders. Neilsen (1962) analyzed aphasic symptoms and organized them according to perception, motor, and language disorders. Listed as a subgroup of the latter classification, amnesic aphasia in its mild form was seen as characterized by word-retrieval problems with nouns and, in its more severe form, by retrieval difficulties with verbs, adjectives, and other parts of speech. Weisenberg and McBride (1964) reported that both receptive and expressive processes are often disturbed in aphasia. These authors, however, classified aphasic disorders as either (a) predominantly expressive, (b) predominantly receptive, (c) both expressive and receptive, or (d) amnesic. The latter class was typified by major difficulty in evoking words in the presence of relatively satisfactory receptive abilities. Cohn (1970) defined amnesic aphasia as an inability to name a specific common object without a loss of the ability to repeat the word after it has been presented, to describe its use, or to designate it through circumlocutions.

Other classifications of naming disorders have been based on neurological models. Geschwind (1967), for example, identified the following four naming-disorder syndromes based on their underlying neurological substrata and related them to different error patterns: (a) the classic anomic disorder with lesions, usually in the "dominant angular gyrus region," leading to difficulties with constrained and spontaneous naming in the presence of good comprehension ability; (b) disconnection syndromes characterized by impaired ability to put a spoken name with a stimulus or a stimulus with a spoken name; (c) nonaphasic misnaming resulting from diffuse disorders of the brain, as seen in patients whose spontaneous speech is usually normal but evidences gross errors in confrontation naming; and (d) hysterical and malingering anomia typified by patients with normal spontaneous speech but gross global breakdowns in confrontation naming. Patients in the latter group have difficulty naming the simplest objects and express great concern over their inability to retrieve the target word.

Luria's classification of aphasia (cited in Hatfield, 1981) rests on an identification of the cortical functions implicated. According to Luria (1980), normal cortical activity is governed by the "law of strength" (p. 516). That is, a strong stimulus evokes a strong response, whereas a weak stimulus results in a weak response. However, in inhibitory states or under pathological conditions this "law of strength" phenomenon may be altered, resulting in an equalizing phase wherein both strong and weak stimuli generate equally strong responses. Specifically, with respect to the underlying neurological dysfunction of the amnesic or anomic aphasia, Luria stated the following:

> If such a pathological state affects the speech areas of the cortex and, in particular, the most complex "tertiary" zones (the parieto-occipito-temporal zones of the cortex of the left hemisphere), so that their mode of working is switched to that of the "inhibitory" or "equalizing" phase, naturally the traces of connections excited by each pattern or word will appear with equal probability and choosing the right word (name) will be much more difficult. (p. 516)

The high incidence of word-finding problems among adults with neurological disorders has been widely documented. In their classification of aphasics, Schuell and Jenkins (1959) reported that all patients showed impaired word-finding skills. Canter (1972) stated that word-retrieval disturbances are the most consistent problems observed in the various syndromes of adult aphasia. Benson (1983) indicated that disorders of word finding are the most common aphasic disorder, occurring to some degree in almost all aphasics. He has maintained that not all anomias are the same and has identified the following types of adult anomia: word-production anomia, word-selection anomia, semantic anomia, category-specific anomia, modality-specific anomia, disconnection anomia, anomia of dementia, nonaphasic misnaming, and psychogenic anomia. In describing contemporary classifications of aphasic syndromes ("nonfluent" aphasias, aphemias, and fluent aphasias), Goodglass (1981) made consistent reference to patients having difficulty "naming on request" and, in many cases, experiencing problems in finding words in "free conversation" (pp. 8-14).

Although aphasiologists have established varying constructs of aphasia and highlighted different aspects of aphasia in their classifications, all of them have identified word-finding problems as a correlate of aphasia. Additionally, in spite of disagreement on the specific nature of this disorder and variation in the names employed to describe it (e.g., verbal amnesia, aphasia, amnesic aphasia, anomia, word-finding deficits, and word-retrieval problems), some consensus exists on the fundamental properties and behavioral manifestations of word-finding difficulties. Most would agree that, although this disorder is not unitary in nature, it involves difficulty finding words in either specific or spontaneous naming situations in the presence of good comprehension of the intended word. The nature of the words that are most difficult to find appears to vary with the patient. For example, mild forms of word-finding problems may be reflected in a breakdown in nouns only, whereas more severe cases may be seen as breakdowns in retrieval of other parts of speech as well. Analysis of the residual language abilities of some patients with word-finding problems reflects circumlocutory or functional descriptive speech, literal or verbal paraphasias, and a high incidence of empty words such as "thing" and "stuff."

WORD-FINDING PROBLEMS IN YOUNGER POPULATIONS

Studies of word-finding skills in younger populations have focused primarily on children, with few investigations of word-finding skills in adolescents. Thus, our understanding of word skills in adolescents has been gleaned from these child investigations. Johnson and Myklebust (1967) presented one of the first documentations of word-finding problems in children with learning disabilities. These children were described as having a primary deficit in "reauditorization" and "word selection." Further, these children had good comprehension and recognition skills for words, but experienced difficulty retrieving words for spontaneous usage. According to Johnson and Myklebust, these children "try to relate happenings, but give up in desperation because they cannot remember how to say what they have in mind. In school these children raise their hands to respond, but by the time the teacher calls on them, they have forgotten what they intended to say" (p. 115).

Wiig and Semel (1976, 1980, 1984) have continuously documented the characteristics, assessment procedures, and remedial strategies for children and adolescents with word-finding problems. Their research has consistently served to impress upon the field the need to routinely consider this expressive language disorder in language evaluations. Specifically, Wiig and Semel (1984) suggested that children with learning disabilities may manifest "difficulties in recalling and retrieving specific words accurately and speedily when they are asked to name pictures or objects, find proper names, describe past experiences or events, or speak in spontaneous conversation" (p. 110). Based on their research, the authors have identified the following characteristics in the connected speech of children with word-finding problems: (a) prolonged pauses and circumlocutions; (b) use of empty place holders and stereotyped meaningless phrases; (c) excessive use of starters, indefinites, and words lacking specificity; and (d) redundant and perseverative repetitions and substitutions of prefixes and suffixes.

After an analysis of the processes involved in word finding, Leonard et al. (1983) proposed two hypotheses for describing the source of this language disorder in children with linguistic impairment—the storage hypothesis and the retrieval hypothesis. The former suggests that word-finding difficulties are the result of poor storage of lexical items in long-term memory. In contrast, the retrieval hypothesis proposes that the deficit is due not to poor storage of lexical representations but to impaired accessing of those labels when needed for oral expression. In a series of studies investigating these two hypotheses, Kail and Leonard (1986) reported that it was an unelaborate representation of words that caused word-finding deficits in the language-impaired students (exhibiting both comprehension and production disorders) they studied.

In her investigations of children's word-finding skills, German (1985b, [1986] 1989) has focused on establishing word-finding profiles in constrained and spontaneous naming contexts. In the former, four word-finding profiles have been identified with respect to accuracy and time: *slow and inaccurate, fast and inaccurate, slow and accurate,* and *fast and accurate*. In addition, German (1987a, in press) noted that children with word-finding problems manifested one of three profiles in spontaneous naming on a picture description task: (a) adequate production (story descriptions of adequate length) with many characteristics of word-finding problems (a significant number of repetitions, reformulations, target-word substitutions, empty words, insertions, delays, and time fillers); (b) reduced production (story descriptions of limited length) with an absence of the characteristics of word-finding difficulties; or (c) reduced production with high incidence of the characteristics of word-finding difficulties. Experimental comparisons of word-finding profiles in constrained naming versus discourse appear to support clinical observations that students with word-finding problems may manifest word-finding difficulties in either or both of these situational contexts. German (1987b), in a comparative study of children with and without word-finding problems, reported word-finding profiles that suggest variation in naming skills across situational contexts. The largest subgroup of language-disordered children studied did manifest word-finding difficulties in both constrained naming and discourse. The second largest subgroup manifested word-finding deficits in discourse but exhibited adequate word-finding skills in constrained naming. The third subgroup manifested word-finding difficulties in naming but adequate word-finding skills in discourse. She concluded that a clinician observing the naming skills of children with word-finding disorders across contexts could expect to observe one of three naming profiles: (1) naming difficulties in both constrained and spontaneous speaking situations; (2) word-finding deficits in spontaneous language situations, with little difficulty retrieving single words on constrained naming tasks; or (3) word-finding deficits in retrieving single words, with little difficulty in word finding in discourse.

WHO HAS WORD-FINDING PROBLEMS?

Investigations of students' word-finding problems have focused primarily on four subject groups: those with learning disabilities, those with reading problems or dyslexia, those with language impairment, and those evidencing fluency disorders. The following is a review of the word-finding research related to each of these populations of exceptional learners.

LEARNING DISABILITIES

Results of investigations of word-finding skills in learning disabled populations have supported Johnson and Myklebust's (1967) assertion that children with learning disabilities manifest difficulties in this area. Comparing the word-finding performance of learning disabled and normal elementary school age students, German (1979) reported significantly more word-finding errors among learning disabled subjects on low-frequency words in two of the three stimulus contexts employed. In a second investigation, German (1984) contrasted the word-finding skills of learning disabled students with and without word-finding problems with the naming skills of normal achievers. Results showed that learning disabled children with word-finding problems manifested significantly more errors, secondary characteristics, longer completion times, and unique substitution types, whereas the performance of learning disabled children without word-finding problems was similar to that of their normally achieving peers. Based on these findings, German concluded that not all learning disabled children have word-finding problems. To identify the subgroup of students who demonstrate this productive language disorder, assessment of word-finding skills in learning disabled populations is necessary.

Lewis and Kass (1982) investigated the labeling and recall skills of learning disabled and average students. In this study, the learning disabled students produced fewer appropriate labels and more inappropriate labels on object and picture-naming tasks. Although termed *hyperexcitability,* the descriptions of the learning disabled students' naming behavior were not unlike responses observed in learning disabled children manifesting word-finding problems in constrained naming tasks. In an examination of learning disabled students' retrieval skills and oral reading errors, Blumenthal (1980) found poorer performance by the experimental group on the rapid, automatized naming test employed by Denckla and Rudel (1974). As a result, Blumenthal concluded that retrieval accuracy was a problem for the learning disabled subjects. Garnett and Fleischner's (1983) investigation of the relationship between basic-fact performance and automatization skills in normal and learning disabled children also revealed reduced performance by the latter subjects on the rapid, automatized naming test used by Denckla and Rudel (1974).

Those studies that have investigated word-finding difficulties in adolescents with learning disabilities have also pointed to naming difficulties (Wiig, LaPointe, & Semel, 1977). For example, Wiig and Semel (1975) reported picture-naming deficits in adolescents with learning disabilities on a visual confrontation naming task, with learning disabled subjects manifesting significantly more errors and longer response times than their normally achieving counterparts. In addition, these authors found that the learning disabled subjects scored significantly lower than their normally learning counterparts on the Verbal Opposites test of the *Detroit Tests of Learning Aptitude* (Baker & Leland, 1967), leading to the conclusion that "anomia and verbal paraphasia associated with learning disabilities may persist into adolescence" (p. 214). White (1979; cited in Wiig & Becker-Caplan, 1984) investigated the naming skills of adolescents with and without dyslexia. Dyslexic adolescents manifested more verbal descriptions and word-association errors on a picture-naming task than their normally achieving peers.

READING DISORDERS

Numerous investigators have examined word-finding skills in subjects with reading disorders. Although some studies have not reported evidence of word-finding deficits in children with reading problems (Katz & Shankweiler, 1985; Perfetti, Finger, & Hogaboam, 1978; Stanovich, 1981), most investigations have indicated a higher incidence of word-finding deficits in reading-disordered children. Eakin and Douglas (1971), for example, reported that children with poor oral reading skills demonstrated more difficulty on automatized naming tasks than their normally learning controls. Similarly, in their research attempts to delineate factors underlying dyslexia, Mattis, French, and Rapin (1975) identified a language-disordered syndrome of dyslexia in which word-finding problems constituted a critical factor.

Using the Oldfield-Wingfield *Picture Naming Test,* Denckla and Rudel (1976a) studied the word-finding abilities of (a) dyslexic children with minimal brain dysfunction (MBD), (b) nondyslexic MBD children, and (c) normal learners. Results showed that the dyslexic MBD subjects demonstrated longer response times and made more errors on the picture-naming tasks than did the nondyslexic MBD subjects, whose naming scores and response latencies fell within the normal range. Since the Oldfield-Wingfield *Picture Naming Test* is considered a sensitive technique for measuring residual dysphasia in adults, Denckla and Rudel concluded that the dyslexic group in their study was subtly dysphasic. In a second investigation, the authors (1976b) reported that the dyslexics required significantly longer response times than their nondyslexic MBD and normal peers on a rapid, automatized naming test. Wolf's (1980) investigation of the naming behavior of poor and good readers between the ages of 6 and 11 revealed that the former were distinguished by the following naming patterns: (a) greater discrepancies between receptive and expressive measures; (b) greater deficiencies in phonological fluency and letter naming; (c) erratic naming unaffected by target-word frequency; and (d) substantial response differences.

Results of correlational studies have also shown a strong relationship between reading and word-finding skills. Jansky and DeHirsch's (1973) reports of clinical observations indicated that poor readers have difficulty evoking auditory equivalents of printed words. Based on these observations, the authors included a picture-naming subtest in their predictive battery designed to identify students with reading problems. Next to letter naming, the picture-naming subtest was the most powerful predictor of those children who were likely to fail in reading in the second grade. Semel and Wiig (1980) cited moderate correlations ($-.44$ for time and $.43$ for accuracy) between the Spache Reading Passage test and the Producing Names on Confrontation subtest of the *Clinical Evaluation of Language Functions* (CELF) (Semel & Wiig, 1980), indicating a significant relationship between reading and rapid, automatized naming skills for 30 learning disabled subjects. Similarly, Wolf (1980) reported substantial correlations ($.74$) between the naming and reading tests employed in an investigation of the naming behavior of poor and good readers between the ages of 6 and 11. Wolf (1980) concluded, therefore, that the relationship between reading and word-retrieval processes is so strong that a dysfunction in one may predict a dysfunction in the other process.

Two investigators have attempted to unravel the correlation between word finding and reading consistently reported in the studies discussed previously. One study explored the relationship between word finding and subtypes of reading disabilities. Felton (1983) categorized subjects using the *Boder Test of Reading-Spelling Patterns* (Dysphonetic, Mixed, Dyseidetic, and Nonspecific) before examining their word-finding ability on a battery of naming tests. The results failed to support a differential relationship between word finding and the subtypes of reading disabilities studied. Rather, the presence of significant word-finding problems across all four reading subtypes was indicated. The second investigation examined the relationship between type of retrieval task and different reading contexts. Wolf, Bally, and Morris (1984) reported on a longitudinal investigation that examined the relationship between different reading skills (word recognition, comprehension) and word-retrieval abilities (continuous naming in automatized and nonautomatized naming contexts) of average and impaired readers, kindergarten through second grade. While average readers were found to undergo various stages in naming skills, impaired readers showed a lesser degree of change in naming over time and a retrieval rate for all naming categories significantly slower than that of first-grade average readers. In addition, a change in the nature of the retrieval/reading relationship of average readers across the three grades differed from that observed in the reading impaired group. Both groups evidenced weaker relationships between reading comprehension and retrieval with no significant relationship between nonautomatized symbol speed and reading by grade 2. However, no similarities were noted between the groups with respect to automatized stimuli retrieval, oral reading, and word recognition. That is, whereas average readers' correlations decreased with grade, those of impaired readers increased with grade. These findings were interpreted as indicating that in impaired readers' reading development, automatic retrieval subprocesses may maintain a greater and more prolonged importance.

LANGUAGE DISORDERS

Word-finding problems have also been identified in children with language disorders. Investigations by both Rubin and Liberman (1983) and Wiig, Semel, and Nystrom (1982) revealed significantly below-age-level performance by language-impaired students on word-finding tasks. Leonard et al. (1983) contrasted the naming performance of 6- to 10-year-old children with and without language disorders. Although differences in accuracy were not noted, students demonstrating language problems took longer to name pictures than their age mates. Similarly, Fried-Oken (1984) contrasted the naming abilities of non–learning disabled language-impaired children with those of normally learning subjects ranging in age from 4 to 9 years. Using a unique dual trial procedure, the author presented 50 drawings of target words balanced for word frequency and semantic category. Incorrect responses were classified into two groups. Group 1 included (a) misnaming in only one trial and (b) errors followed by self-corrections; Group 2 included errors produced in both trials. Difference in naming skills between the two groups was reported because language-impaired children manifested longer response times and made more errors in each response group. Specifically, language-impaired children committed 61.4% of all the single trial errors classified in Group 1—the response group that the author reported as indicating naming problems. To determine the role that retrieval deficits play in word-finding problems of language-disordered children, Kail and Leonard (1986) studied language-disordered children with both language comprehension and production disorders. They concluded that, for these children with both comprehension and production disorders, word-finding difficulties were not due to retrieval deficits, but rather were the result of poor representation of words in semantic memory. Additional investigations are needed to clarify the nature of word-finding difficulties in language-disordered children. In particular, investigations contrasting word-finding skills in language-disordered children with and without comprehension disorders would help clarify word-finding difficulties due to underlying storage versus retrieval deficits.

FLUENCY DISORDERS

Investigators have also focused on the relationship between word-finding skills and fluency disorders, particularly stuttering. Weuffen (1961), who conducted one of the first studies of this type, compared subjects' word-retrieval abilities through an experimental method that generated a ratio of the number of words written to the number of words spoken. A significantly larger number of children with word-finding problems were found in the stuttering group than in the nonstuttering control group. Telser (1971) also studied word-finding skills among stutterers and nonstutterers. Using an experimental measure, the *Northwestern Word Latency Test,* Telser evaluated the word-finding performance of 20 stuttering and 20 normally speaking children ranging in age from 5 to 12 years. Results showed significantly longer mean response latencies in the stuttering group, with 55% of the stuttering population classified as having word-finding problems compared to only 15% of the nonstuttering subjects. Boysen and Cullinan (1971) examined object-naming latencies in stuttering and nonstuttering children. Their findings were inconsistent with those reported by Telser (1971), indicating that, when considering mean latencies, the response times for stutterers tended to be shorter than those of nonstutterers. The authors concluded that stutterers, at least in the age range studied, may not experience more word-finding problems on the average than their normally fluent counterparts.

In summary, studies of children's word finding have focused on these problems in learning disabled students, non–learning disabled students with language impairment, students with reading problems, and students diagnosed as stutterers. For the most part, the results of these investigations have identified word-finding difficulties as a problem concomitant with disorders in all four areas—learning, reading, language, and possibly stuttering. However, additional investigations are still needed to clarify the nature of the relationship between word finding and specific academic, language, or fluency disorders. In addition, studies that focus on adolescents with word-finding difficulties are needed in order to clarify the presence of this language disorder in the older student. The presence of this expressive language disorder in adolescents and young adults has been reported clinically. However, investigations directed toward this population would provide experimental documentation of the prolonged nature of this expressive language disorder and the continuation of word-finding disorders into adulthood. Use of the TAWF to investigate these research questions would be very appropriate. Through its standardized systematic procedures for assessing constrained naming skills, the TAWF will contribute to future research efforts in these areas.

DIAGNOSTIC MODEL FOR ASSESSING WORD-FINDING SKILLS

The TAWF is based on a diagnostic model drawn from the word-finding literature. The model incorporates indices to define word-finding problems and considers those variables identified as influencing word-finding behavior during assessment.

WORD-FINDING INDICES

Word-finding problems have been defined according to one or a combination of the following three indices: accuracy score, response time, and substitution type (response analysis).

Accuracy Score

Accuracy scores are a measurement of the number of target words an individual names correctly on the first response during the word-finding assessment. In contrast to the response-time measurement, this index provides insights into the selection process itself. As a result, it allows for follow-up analyses of target-word substitutions that may aid in identifying the naming strategies employed by the subject. The usefulness of the accuracy index in word-finding assessment has been verified in numerous investigations. Specifically, it has been used to assess word-retrieval skills in adult aphasics (Gardner, 1974a; Goodglass, Klein, Carey, & Jones, 1966; Rochford & Williams, 1965). This naming index has differentiated naming skills among age groups in normal populations, with children's naming accuracy improving with age (Wiegel-Crump & Dennis, 1986). German ([1986] 1989) reported a significant correlation ($r = .51$) between accuracy and age for the 1200 normal subjects in the standardization sample of the *Test of Word Finding* (TWF). The accuracy scores of the normal subjects in the standardization sample increased significantly across grades, reflecting developmental growth. This index has also differentiated word-finding skills in special populations, including students with learning disabilities (German, 1979, 1984; Wiig & Semel, 1976), reading disorders (Denckla & Rudel, 1976b; Wolf, 1980), language disorders (Fried-Oken, 1984), and word-finding disorders (German, [1986] 1989).

The accuracy score is the main index utilized in the TAWF. It consists of a total raw score converted into percentile ranks or standard scores, thereby enabling the examiner to compare the naming accuracy of the subject with that of grade and/or age mates in the standardization sample.

Response Time

Response-time evaluation determines the time it takes a subject to find the target word or an approximation thereof. This index has been used to assess word-retrieval skills in adults (Goodglass, Theurkauf, & Wingfield, 1984; Newcombe, Oldfield, & Wingfield, 1965; Oldfield & Wingfield, 1965; Wingfield, 1968) and also has been used to identify word-finding abilities in children with fluency problems (Telser & Rutherford, 1970), reading disorders (Denckla & Rudel, 1976b), and language disorders (Fried-Oken, 1984; Wiig et al., 1982). In these investigations, both adults and children with word-finding problems manifested significantly longer response times than their control groups, suggesting that extended latencies are characteristic of word-finding disorders. Developmental trends in response time have also been identified. This naming index has differentiated the naming skills of age groups in normal populations, with children's speed of naming improving with age (German, [1986] 1989; Wiegel-Crump & Dennis, 1986).

Two item response time measurements are provided for the analysis of latencies on the TAWF. One is the optional Average Item Response Time (ART) (Total Item Response Time divided by the number of items in Section 1). The other is the Estimated Item Response Time (ERT), a measurement of the number of items on which the subject's response was delayed by 4 seconds or more. If either of these is greater than the grade- or age-level standards of the normal subjects in the standardization sample (presented in the TAWF *Administration, Scoring and Interpretation Manual*), the individual would be assessed as exhibiting significantly slow responses on the TAWF.

Substitution Analysis

Analysis of substitution types manifested when a person has difficulty naming target words is a useful informal evaluation to identify word-finding problems. This analysis provides insights into semantic structure and semantic processing as well as frequently indicating an individual's general knowledge about a target word he or she is unable to name. Substitution types have been identified in the residual speech of adult aphasics (Coughlan & Warrington, 1978; Rinnert & Whitaker, 1973), and error analyses have proven clinically useful in identifying certain types of adult aphasia (Barton, Maruszewski, & Urrea, 1969; Kohn & Goodglass, 1985; Williams & Canter, 1982) as well as types of adult word-finding disorders (Geschwind, 1967; Rochford, 1971).

Developmental trends in response substitutions manifested by normal children in various naming tasks have been reported. Rochford and Williams (1962) studied the relationship between nominal dysphasia and acquisition of vocabulary in childhood and reported a similarity between the errors made by dysphasic patients and those made by children. Rudel, Denckla, Broman, and Hirsch (1980) used six categories to characterize normally learning children's naming errors (circumlocutions, paraphasic substitutions, paraphasic part-whole responses, half-right paraphasic errors, phonemic-sequencing errors, and perceptual errors). They found that younger children tended to produce more "don't know" responses or unclassifiable or perceptual errors, whereas older children tended to produce more substitutions which were similar to error responses made by aphasics (circumlocutions and paraphasic substitutions). Part-whole and half-right paraphasic errors and phonemic errors were used to a lesser degree and reflected smaller increases with age. Wiegel-Crump and Dennis (1986) analyzed word-finding errors across age groups (6–14 years) and reported differences between younger and older children's naming responses. Younger children produced more symptomatic substitutions. In addition, although responses for all ages were for the most part semantically related to the target word, the number of elements shared between the target word and the substitution increased with age. Younger children also produced associations to the target word, whereas older students did not. Responses phonemically similar but not semantically similar were not present at any age. The findings from these investigations suggest that a developmental dimension may be operating in the type of response made to word lapses in naming tasks.

Analyses of substitutions responses in special populations have revealed differential response patterns. Denckla and Rudel (1976a) performed an error analysis on the incorrect responses manifested by their dyslexic and nondyslexic MBD subjects. Using three categories—circumlocutions, wrong names, and not known—they reported that 61% of the error types made by dyslexic subjects were circumlocutions, compared to only 32% in the nondyslexic MBD group. In addition, the nondyslexic MBD subjects manifested significantly more incorrect name responses than did their normally learning or dyslexic peers. Similarly, in a study of adolescent dyslexics, White (1979; cited in Wiig & Becker-Caplan, 1984) found that dyslexic subjects manifested three times as many circumlocutions and word-association responses as did their nondyslexic age mates on a picture-naming test.

Studying the naming patterns of learning disabled and normally learning students (8 to 12 years old) when naming to pictures, open-ended sentences, and description, German (1982) measured the relative importance of the following substitution categories by percentage of occurrence: synonym, semantically related, phonemically related, similar function, functional attribute, verb substitution, visual misidentification, visually similar, compositional, acceptable substitution, initial sound, "I don't know," and attention to part responses. Three substitution patterns unique to learning disabled children were identified. These included substitutions that shared functional features with the target word *(book holder* for *shelf);* substitutions that shared visual attributes with the referent of the target word *(string* for *rein);* and substitutions that included phonemic features (initial sounds) of the target word *(s, s, sail* for *sail)* or of a discarded response *(br, br, comb* for *comb).* In a second investigation, German (1984) again found substitutions sharing functional and phonemic attributes of the target word to be unique to learning disabled children with word-finding problems. However, while visual attributes did not differentiate the groups in this investigation, circumlocutory-type responses were noted as a unique naming pattern. Wiig and Semel (1984) recommended the following response categories for classifying naming errors of subjects with language disabilities: phonological realization, semantic realization, phonemic/semantic, descriptive/circumlocution, and indefinite reference.

Fried-Oken (1984) also analyzed error patterns in her investigation of the word-finding skills of language-impaired and normally language-learning children. She investigated the percentage of incorrect responses produced in each of the following error categories: phonological, perceptual, semantic, circumlocution, ordination, noninformative response, and combination error categories such as semantic + perceptual and semantic + perceptual + phonological. Regardless of language ability, both groups most frequently produced semantic + perceptual error types, noninformative error types, and semantic error types, indicating that the language-impaired subjects had acquired the same word-finding strategies for confrontation naming as the normally language-learning children. Fried-Oken concluded that a limited use of naming strategies rather than an absence of naming strategies characterized the language-impaired children in the investigation.

Identification of response patterns has both diagnostic and remedial implications. Diagnostically, response patterns may aid in the differentiation of various types of expressive language disorders, while remedially they can provide guidelines for choosing appropriate cuing and organizing techniques. In addition, because different naming patterns emerged in different investigations, the use of particular substitution types may be influenced by the nature of the naming task and may be specific to an individual's lexical storage system. Error-pattern analysis, then, is specific to the word-finding assessment employed and unique to the person under study.

The TAWF provides the examiner with an informal evaluation procedure for analyzing error responses on the various naming sections. This response-analysis model was derived from psycholinguistic studies of the different semantic and lexical relationships between words (Evens, Litowitz, Markowitz, Smith, & Werner, 1983; Lyons, 1977; Riegel, 1970). In addition, the model incorporates substitution types drawn from adult and child literature as well as response categories generated from the adolescents and adults with word-finding problems in the TAWF standardization sample. Response categories for Sections 1, 2, 3, and 5 consist of the following general categories: semantic, perceptual, nonspecific words, circumlocutions, substitution plus self-correction, and no response. Response categories for Section 4 include these general categories along with response categories that are unique to the Picture Naming: Verbs section: innovative verb responses, pro-verbal action responses, related noun responses, root-word responses, and picture labeling. (See the TAWF *Administration, Scoring and Interpretation Manual* for descriptions and examples of all of the response categories.)

The informal analysis of substitution types should follow the formal accuracy and time assessments. It should be completed on individuals whose accuracy score is greater than one standard deviation below the mean of the normal subjects in the standardization sample or is in the borderline range. The informal nature of this assessment gives the examiner an opportunity to tailor a substitution analysis to a particular person under study without interfering with the formal assessment of that person's accuracy and response latencies on the TAWF.

Secondary Characteristics

Secondary characteristics refer to those behaviors that often accompany efforts to verbalize target words in constrained naming situations or in discourse. Two types of secondary characteristics—*gestures* (e.g., mime of the target word, tapping, pointing, or nonverbal indication of frustration) and *extra verbalizations* ("it's a," "oh," "I know it," etc.)—may be present when somebody is manifesting word-finding difficulties. Based on a study of the development of gestures in children, Barten (1979) identified five gesture types: deictic, instrumental, expressive, enactive, and depictive. Further, Johnson and Myklebust (1967) clinically observed the use of these gesture types along with extra verbalizations when learning disabled children are having difficulty retrieving words. According to these authors, younger children may use acoustic representations of the target word while others may use gestures or pantomime to communicate their message. More specifically, Wiig and Semel (1984, p. 112) indicated that learning disabled children may produce "idiosyncratic hand movements" or manifest "facial grimaces" or "hit the table," "swing a leg," or "tap a rhythm with one foot" when they are struggling to find a word to express their thoughts. Fried-Oken (1984) categorized these behaviors as error types, labeling gestures as "nonverbal circumlocutions" and comments as "noninformative responses." Classifying these behaviors as secondary characteristics of word-finding difficulties, German (1982, 1984) conducted analyses on the frequency of occurrence of gestures and extra verbalizations in the naming behavior of language-impaired children with learning disabilities. Results indicated that children with word-finding problems manifested significantly more gestures and extra verbalizations on those naming tasks where they manifested more errors and longer response times. They did not manifest these behaviors to any great degree on those naming tasks in which they performed similarly to their normally language-learning counterparts (German, 1985a).

Extra verbalizations are comments that are made on the language process itself during the word-finding block. These may be metacognitive comments ("I know it, but can't think of it") that indicate an individual's knowledge of the target word or metalinguistic comments ("It starts with an 'f' ") that aid the search for the target word by providing cues for naming. The gestural behavior appears to give nonverbal support to the word-finding process. For example, one subject, in an attempt to name "chopsticks," mimed eating.

These findings emphasize the need to look beyond the actual word-finding task when assessing word-finding abilities. The TAWF provides the examiner with an informal observation procedure for systematically noting the presence of these secondary word-finding characteristics during the naming tasks (see the TAWF *Administration, Scoring and Interpretation Manual).* These observations of secondary characteristics in naming can play an important role in both compensatory programming and remediation for the individuals with word-finding disorders. First, identification of those secondary characteristics that are specific to a particular person's naming behavior (use of gestures or extra verbalizations or both) should be communicated to family members and teachers to help them identify when the person is having word-finding difficulties. The presence of either of these secondary characteristics should signal to the listener that a particular speaker is manifesting word-finding difficulties; the listener might then use compensatory techniques to aid the word retrieval at that moment (multiple choice, initial sound, or extended time to retrieve the target word). Second, remediation should focus on redirecting the energy expended on those secondary characteristics, often distracting and nonconstructive, to naming strategies that will facilitate retrieval.

In summary, observing subjects as well as listening to their comments on the language process during the naming tasks may (a) clarify whether they know the target word, thus indicating whether the noted naming difficulties represent a word-finding problem, (b) provide evidence of the cues used during the naming process, and (c) give insights into the level of frustration experienced during the naming task. Such information can help clarify the language intervention necessary for a particular person (German, 1985a).

VARIABLES IN WORD-FINDING ASSESSMENT

SITUATIONAL CONTEXT

Situational context refers to the constrained (single-word naming) versus spontaneous (naming in discourse) nature of the naming task. There are at least two means of studying word-finding problems. One is to analyze the retrieval system through constrained naming tasks such as naming to pictures, naming to open-ended sentences, and naming to description. The other consists of studying word-finding skills in discourse by analyzing language samples elicited through picture description, story-telling tasks, or dialogue. The literature on adult aphasia has clearly stressed the need to analyze not only the "nominative," but also the narrative aspects of speech (Luria, 1966). Canter (1972) observed clinically that word-finding skills vary as a function of the situational context and that this variance may be related to the type of aphasia present in the adult. Although adult studies have primarily employed the constrained naming type of task (Newcombe et al., 1965; Oldfield & Wingfield, 1965; Rochford & Williams, 1965), studies of word-finding skills in connected speech have also been reported. For example, investigating the influence of two situational contexts on the naming performance of adult aphasics, Williams and Canter (1982) reported that subjects with Broca's aphasia performed significantly better on confrontation naming tasks while Wernicke's patients did significantly better on picture description tasks. Marshall (1976) observed the following five types of word-retrieval behaviors in the connected speech of adult aphasics: delay, semantic association, phonetic association, description, and generalization.

For the most part, child studies of word-finding performance have employed constrained naming tasks (Denckla & Rudel, 1976a, 1976b; German, 1979, 1984; Wiig & Semel, 1976; Wiig et al., 1982). Thus, these investigations explored whether the subject could successfully name a single word rather than find words in discourse. Studies of children's word-finding behavior in discourse are rare. However, Wiig and Semel (1984) clinically identified the following characteristics of children's word-finding behavior in discourse: pauses, interjections, repetitions, and revisions or repairs. Furthermore, Wiig and Becker-Caplan (1984) suggested that such pragmatic variables as "speaker-listener relationship, informational load, and communication medium (e.g., face-to-face, over the telephone, in writing)" (p. 13) affect naming skills in discourse. In an investigation of children's word-finding skills in discourse, German (1987a) analyzed the language samples of normal and language-disordered children, ages 7 to 12, for total verbalizations and modified mean length of utterance, as well as the following word-finding characteristics: reformulations, starters, repetitions, incompletes, time fillers, empty words, delays, and substitutions. Two spontaneous language profiles emerged as being unique to children with word-finding problems. The cardinal characteristic of the first profile was a reduction in amount of oral language with few word-finding behaviors except for the presence of many incompletes. The second profile was represented by a speech sample of adequate length; but unlike the first, it included more of the characteristics typical of children who display word-finding problems, including repetitions, reformulations, and substitutions. Based on these findings, German (1987a) concluded that children with word-finding problems may manifest word-finding difficulties in discourse. In addition, experimental comparisons (German, 1987b) of word-finding profiles in constrained versus spontaneous naming supported clinical observations that students with word-finding problems may manifest word-finding difficulties in either or both of these situational contexts. Thus, she recommended that word-finding assessment include an analysis of discourse to complement the traditional assessment in the constrained naming situation.

Since the TAWF assesses word-finding skills in the constrained situational context only, it should be followed with an informal analysis of word-finding skills in discourse. The individual's picture descriptions, spontaneous stories, or conversations could be used to provide the speech corpus needed for the assessment. A model for analyzing word-finding skills in discourse is provided in the *Test of Word Finding in Discourse* (German, in press). Examiners could informally apply this model to the language samples of adolescents and adults to describe an individual's word-finding skills in discourse.

STIMULUS CONTEXT

Stimulus context refers to the nature of the naming task used to assess word-finding skills in constrained naming. Difficulty hierarchies in stimulus context have been reported in the word-finding ability of adults (Barton et al., 1969; Goodglass & Stuss, 1979). The impact of stimulus context on naming in the normal learning population has also been explored. Rudel et al. (1980) investigated the influence of stimulus context (tactile naming, picture naming, naming to open-ended sentences, and naming to description) on the naming skills of normally learning children between the ages of 5 and 11. Results showed a difficulty hierarchy for the naming sections employed that differed in accuracy and response time. For accuracy, tactile naming appeared the easiest, followed by open-ended sentences and picture naming, with naming to description being the most difficult. With respect to time, however, the easiest task was the slowest. Tactile naming, therefore, resulted in the longest times, followed by naming to description and picture naming, with open-ended sentences emerging as the fastest. Naming differences as a function of stimulus context was more typical of the younger subjects, since by age 11 the naming accuracy of normal children appeared no longer to be influenced by stimulus context. For the older subjects, frequency of error was the same for each condition. Wiegel-Crump and Dennis (1986) also looked at the development of word finding as it relates to different naming contexts (semantic description, rhyming, and picture naming). They reported a hierarchy of difficulty for all ages where naming to a rhyme was more difficult than naming to pictures or naming to description. Naming to pictures was easiest for the younger groups but not for the oldest groups.

Extending this line of research to learning disabled students, German (1979, 1984) investigated the impact of stimulus context on accuracy and speed of naming. A hierarchy of difficulty for stimulus context was identified for both indices. With respect to accuracy, condition difficulty in order from easiest to hardest was as follows: naming to pictures, naming to open-ended sentences, and naming to description. Difficulty order for response time differed in that open-ended sentences emerged as the easiest, followed by naming to pictures. The most difficult was found to be naming to description. Examining the effects of stimulus contexts on dyslexic children's word-finding skills, Rudel, Denckla, and Broman (1981) found that both dyslexic and nondyslexic learning disabled children performed more poorly than normals in naming to pictures, descriptions, sentence completion, and naming objects. The dyslexic subjects found the naming to description and the sentence-completion tasks more difficult than the picture-naming and haptic conditions, a finding reported by the authors as not surprising since dyslexics have been noted to exhibit auditory sequencing problems.

Children's word-finding skills have also been assessed with the context of the "rapid automatized naming test." This test format, which requires a person to rapidly name pictures representing such familiar stimuli as objects, colors, numbers, or letters, has been found useful for differentiating word-finding skills in normal children (Denckla & Rudel, 1974), as well as in children with dyslexia (Denckla & Rudel, 1976b), with oral reading problems (Eakin & Douglas, 1971), with learning problems (Blumenthal, 1980), and with math difficulties (Garnett & Fleischner, 1983). Wiig et al. (1982) investigated word-finding skills (measuring both accuracy and speed) of language and learning disabled children on two other rapid naming tests, the Naming Picture Objects test and the Producing Names on Confrontation subtest of the *Clinical Evaluation of Language Functions* (CELF) (Semel & Wiig, 1980). These rapid naming tests differentiated the experimental from the control groups with respect to speed and accuracy of naming.

Another context used to assess word-finding skills in children is the word-association task (Wiig & Becker-Caplan, 1984). Unlike the constrained and spontaneous naming contexts, this task requires the subject to name as many words as possible that represent a specific category (McCarthy, 1970; Semel & Wiig, 1980), that start with a specific letter ("f" test), or that the student can remember (free-association task) (Baker & Leland, 1967). Clinically, students with word-finding problems have been observed to manifest reduced productivity and naming rates on this type of naming task.

The results of these investigations indicate that stimulus contexts can influence naming abilities and that a variety of different naming contexts are useful in identifying word-finding problems in children with language disorders, learning disabilities, and academic deficits. Consequently, multiple naming contexts should be employed when assessing word-finding skills. The TAWF includes items that are representative of four different stimulus contexts: picture naming (intersensory visual to auditory tasks), naming to open-ended sentences, naming to description, and naming to target-word exemplars (intrasensory auditory tasks). Although an individual's word-finding skills can only be assessed informally by section on the TAWF, items representing multiple stimulus contexts are included in the total formal score. Thus, the TAWF provides a broader assessment of word-finding skills than the traditional picture-noun naming task.

NATURE OF THE TARGET WORD

Many descriptions and investigations of the word-finding problems of adult aphasics have focused on the nature of the words that they are unable to retrieve (Ahrens, 1977; Goldstein, 1948; Head, 1926; LeJeune, 1974; Marshall & Newcombe, 1971; Neilsen, 1962; Schuell & Jenkins, 1959; Yamadori & Albert, 1973). Three investigations have examined the impact of different types of target words on naming in the word-finding task.

Goodglass, Klein, Carey, and Jones (1966) attempted to determine whether aphasics found specific semantic categories (objects, colors, numbers, letters, and actions) more difficult than others to name or comprehend. Results of this investigation showed that the difficulty level of the five categories varied depending on whether naming or comprehension was assessed. With respect to naming, letter naming was the easiest, while being the most difficult category for comprehension. The objects category appeared to be the easiest one for comprehension, but the most difficult for naming. In addition, naming skills were distinguished by diagnostic class. That is, Wernicke's and amnesic aphasics were superior in letter naming and inferior in object naming, whereas Broca's aphasics emerged as superior in object naming but poor in letter naming. Based on this differentiation by class, the authors concluded that "it is possible to postulate that the word-finding system is subdivided anatomically according to the psychological character of different word categories" (p. 87).

Gardner (1974a) differentiated the naming behavior of children and adults using different semantic categories when studying object-naming and symbol-naming skills of aphasic patients and children. Children and adult aphasics performed similarly on tasks involving the naming of objects and object parts, but opposite performance on symbol-naming tests was noted for the two groups. That is, aphasic patients experienced most problems with animal names, followed by colors and letters; they encountered the least difficulty with numbers. The children, in turn, had the least difficulty naming animals, then colors and letters; their greatest difficulty was in naming numbers. Gardner (1974b) investigated aphasic and alexic patients' naming and recognition of written symbols. Alexic patients were found to commit more errors in naming words than in naming objects, whereas all anomic patients made more errors in naming pictures of objects than in naming words.

Studies of both normally achieving children and children with learning problems have also indicated differences in naming of various semantic categories. The results of Denckla and Rudel's (1974) investigation of normal children's (5–11 years old) facility in naming different semantic categories in a "rapid automatic naming" task revealed that naming facility did not parallel the developmental order of acquisition of semantic categories. Thus, response times for letters and numbers were shorter than response times for colors and objects, even though the latter categories are acquired earlier. Investigating the word-finding ability of learning disabled children with and without word-finding problems when naming numbers, letters, and colors, German (1985a) also reported group differences in naming as a function of semantic word categories. Learning disabled children with word-finding problems manifested more errors, longer completion times, and more secondary characteristics (gestures and extra verbalizations) on letter- and color-naming tasks while performing similarly to children without word-finding problems on number-naming tasks. Learning disabled children without word-finding problems, in turn, did not differ significantly from their normal counterparts in naming different semantic categories. In general, naming of different semantic categories in "rapid automatic naming" tasks has been reported as being more difficult for children with dyslexia (Denckla & Rudel, 1976b), reading problems (Eakin & Douglas, 1971), and learning problems (Blumenthal, 1980; Garnett & Fleischner, 1983) than for their normally learning peers.

According to these studies, children vary in their ability to name different categories of words, thus emphasizing the need to consider the nature of the target words used when assessing word-finding skills. Therefore, an assessment of word-finding abilities should include items that represent target words across several categories. The TAWF satisfies this requirement by providing the examiner with (a) a naming assessment of noun target words in three contexts (naming to pictures, naming to open-ended sentences, and naming to description); (b) a naming assessment of action words (naming to verbs condition); and (c) a naming assessment of basic object-level and superordinate words (naming to categories). In the TAWF the Picture Naming: Nouns section requires subjects to name target words from 10 semantic categories (school items, household items, games, clothing, food, music, animals, body parts, transportation, and outdoor structures). It is not recommended that performance be evaluated by the semantic category of the target word. However, the composite accuracy score includes these items, thus representing a broad assessment of word finding that employs various categories of target words.

FREQUENCY OF OCCURRENCE OF THE TARGET WORD

Findings from numerous investigations have indicated that the frequency of occurrence of the target word is a significant variable influencing word-finding skills of normal adults (Oldfield, 1966; Oldfield & Wingfield, 1965; Wingfield, 1968). The effect of target words' frequency of occurrence has also been examined in adult aphasics. Wepman et al. (1956) were among the first to identify a frequency effect in naming as they reported that the anomic patient manifests difficulty retrieving low-frequency words in all classes. Similarly, Newcombe et al. (1965) reported latency and accuracy differences as a function of target-word freqency on an object-naming task. As a result, they concluded that detection of naming disorders requires the use of items whose labels represent a certain order of rarity. Using accuracy as an index of retrieval ability, Rochford and Williams (1965) investigated the effect of word frequency upon dysphasics' ability to name common objects, body parts, composite words, and verbs. Their findings showed a relationship between word frequency and word-finding ability: Whatever the group of words studied, the more common items within the group were more available to the aphasic than the rarer ones.

Comparative studies of children and adults have investigated the effects of the frequency variable on naming ability. For example, Rochford and Williams (1962) analyzed naming ability and target-word frequency in acute dysphasics, recovered aphasics, and normally learning children. On one of two object-naming tests, patients' performance was aided by a set of cues. Results indicated that, for all subjects, more learning occurred on the easiest items and that easiness was related to the target word's frequency of usage.

Investigations of the effects of target-word frequency on children's naming have also been reported. However, unlike adult studies, investigations of the frequency variable in children with fluency, reading, language, and learning problems have resulted in inconclusive evidence. Boysen and Cullinan's (1971) investigation of the picture-naming skills of stutterers and nonstutterers revealed response latencies that were negatively correlated with the logarithm of the target word's frequency of occurrence in the language. Telser (1971) reported longer mean response times on higher than on lower frequency words for her sample of stutterers and nonstutterers. Similarly, where Denckla and Rudel (1976a) reported more errors and longer response times on low-frequency words for dyslexic children on a picture-naming task, Wolf (1980) concluded that word frequency did not predict naming errors in her sample of poor readers. Word frequency has been identified as a significant variable in studies of learning disabled children and children with language impairment. That is, German (1979, 1984) reported more errors and longer response times on low-frequency words in her investigations of the naming performance of learning disabled and language-impaired children with word-finding problems. Fried-Oken (1984) and Leonard et al. (1983) also noted a word-frequency effect in the naming abilities of language-disordered and non–language-disordered students, with longer response times manifested on the rarer words. Wiig et al. (1982), however, reported that a picture-naming test consisting of relatively high-frequency words differentiated the word-finding skills of normal and language-disordered children.

Overwhelmingly, studies of adults indicate that low-frequency words are more difficult to retrieve than high-frequency words. In spite of the contrasting findings in child studies, target-word frequency also appears to be an important variable to consider when assessing word-finding skills. In particular it seems necessary to use target words that, although in the student's vocabulary, are challenging. For these reasons, target-word frequency was taken into consideration when selecting the target words for the TAWF. Specifically, the TAWF consists of 107 target words ranked according to their frequency of occurrence in 120 juvenile books surveyed by Thorndike and Lorge (1944) or by their frequency of occurrence in third- through ninth-grade reading texts surveyed and reported in the *American Heritage Word Frequency Book* (Carroll, Davies, & Richman, 1971). Three frequency categories were developed: low, mid, and high frequency. Numerical values for low-frequency target words ranged from 1 to 100 occurrences per 4.5 million words in 120 juvenile books surveyed by Thorndike and Lorge (1944) and 1 to 50 occurrences among 5 million words from third- through ninth-grade reading texts surveyed and reported in the *American Heritage Word Frequency Book* (Carroll et al., 1971). For middle-frequency target words, numerical values ranged from 101 to 200 occurrences per 4.5 million words in 120 juvenile books surveyed by Thorndike and Lorge (1944) and 51 to 100 occurrences among 5 million words from third- through ninth-grade reading texts surveyed and reported in the *American Heritage Word Frequency Book* (Carroll et al., 1971). Finally, numerical values for high-frequency target words ranged from 201 to 700 occurrences per 4.5 million words in 120 juvenile books surveyed by Thorndike and Lorge (1944) and 101 to 250 occurrences among 5 million words from third- through ninth-grade reading texts surveyed and reported in the *American Heritage Word Frequency Book* (Carroll et al., 1971). TAWF vocabulary represents a full spectrum of frequency of occurrence with target words judged to be in the high- (27%), mid- (22%), and low-frequency (51%) categories.

FACILITATING CUES IN WORD FINDING

Cues that facilitate word recall and retrieval have been specified in the normal adult literature (Tulving, 1974; Tulving & Pearlstone, 1966) as well as in investigations of adult aphasics' cuing behavior (Berman & Peelle, 1967; Love & Webb, 1977; Pease & Goodglass, 1978; Wiig & Globus, 1971). Naming cues such as phonetic or semantic prompts have been used to assess word-finding skills in adult aphasics with the *Boston Naming Test* (Kaplan, Goodglass, & Weintraub, 1976). Cuing techniques have also been suggested for assessing word-finding skills in children. Fried-Oken (German & Fried-Oken, 1984) recommended four such cues: general, semantic, phonemic, and verification of knowledge. Wiig and Semel (1984) have also identified a series of word cues useful in remediation to aid word recall and retrieval from long-term memory: associative word cues, phonetic-phonemic word cues, associative-semantic class cues, melodic-stress cues, and multiple-choice cuing.

    Research on the use of cues to facilitate word finding was considered in the development of two stimulus contexts in the TAWF: naming to open-ended sentences and naming to description. Specifically, the open-ended and description sentences were written to incorporate those attributes of target words that have been identified as facilitating cues in investigations of recall and retrieval. Target-word attributes such as semantic class, function, associative strength, location, composition, size, sound, and parts in selected combinations were incorporated in each sentence to aid the subject in finding the target word.

In addition, although the TAWF administration procedure does not allow for formal analysis of the cues that might facilitate naming for a particular subject on the first administration, informal methods can be employed in subsequent administrations and analyses. First, implementation of cuing procedures suggested in the literature can be employed on inaccurate items in a subsequent administration of the TAWF. The examiner can follow the comprehension check with a second administration of the inaccurate items using probes (naming cues) for those target words that the subject missed on the second trial. Second, a review of the response analysis may provide the examiner with insights into a particular person's naming strategies. Generalizing from this analysis, the examiner can determine those naming cues that facilitate or interfere with correct naming. Third, an inventory of the type of sentences on which a subject manifests naming difficulties in the open-ended and description contexts may provide additional insight into the cues that aid word finding or interfere with naming for the particular individual.

CHAPTER TWO

DESCRIPTION OF THE TAWF

The TAWF is based on a diagnostic model of word-finding assessment drawn from child and adult literature in word-finding disorders. Thus, the variables considered in the development of the TAWF format and each set of word-finding items were those reported as influencing word-finding skills. These variables include situational context, stimulus context, target-word frequency, and nature of the target word (semantic categories, prototypicality, and syntax). With respect to prototypicality, Rosch and her colleagues (Rosch, Mervis, Gray, Johnson, & Boyes-Braem, 1976) have documented the influence of core or typical exemplars of verbal categories on performance in many tasks (e.g., an apple is more prototypical of the fruit category than a persimmon). In selecting pictorial and verbal stimuli across all sections of the TAWF, every effort was made to select prototypical exemplars of categories. All contexts and items were statistically analyzed to arrive at a final set of items judged to be most reliable based on the subjects' performance in the item analysis and standardization (see Chapter 3 for item-analysis procedure).

Scoring on the TAWF is based on a total score representative of the combined section scores. However, a discussion of each section is warranted, since each item set represents different naming variables. Below is a description of each naming section.

PICTURE NAMING: NOUNS

The Picture Naming: Nouns section consists of a picture-naming task used to assess accuracy (standard scores and percentile ranks) and speed (estimated and actual item response time) in naming pictorial representations of target words. Picture naming is a traditional format for assessing word-finding skills (Denckla & Rudel, 1976a, 1976b; German, 1979; Kaplan et al., 1976; Oldfield & Wingfield, 1965). Originally, a total of 88 target nouns were identified, drawn from four sources: The *Ginn Intermediate Dictionary* (Morris, 1974), The *Macmillan Dictionary for Children* (Halsey & Morris, 1977), and vocabulary lists from first- through sixth-grade *Ginn Basal Readers* (Johnson, Markert, Shuy, Squire, & Venezky, 1979) and first- through sixth-grade core and additional reading lists drawn from frequently used basal readers as presented by Harris and Jacobson (1972). Vocabulary selection was structured according to five variables identified through clinical observations and research as influencing word-finding skills: syntax, picturability, target-word frequency, syllabication, and semantic categories.

Rigorous item analyses led to the final set of 37 target words. Each of the variables in this section is represented as follows: syntax, nouns = 100%; pictorial ability, visual context = 54%, without visual context = 46%; target-word frequency, low-frequency words = 67%, mid-frequency words = 15%, high-frequency words = 18% (Thorndike count of 120 juvenile books [Thorndike & Lorge, 1944]); syllabication, monosyllabic words = 21.6%, two-syllable words = 27%, three-syllable words = 21.6%, four-syllable words = 8.1%, and compound words = 21.6%; and semantic categories, school instruments = 11%, related to body parts = 8.1%, clothing = 5.4%, animals = 8.1%, related to food = 16.2%, related to music = 8.1%, related to transportation = 16.2%, household items = 10.8%, and outdoor structures = 8.1%.

SENTENCE COMPLETION NAMING

The Sentence Completion Naming section assesses a subject's accuracy (standard scores and percentile ranks) when naming words in an intrasensory auditory context that utilizes a cloze-format procedure. Unique to this naming format is the quality of automaticity which leads to the response. The nature of this naming task has made it a useful format for identifying students with word-finding problems (German, 1979, 1984) and reading disorders (Rudel et al., 1981), as well as adults with naming disorders (Barton et al., 1969). Initially, the Sentence Completion Naming section consisted of 44 items. After rigorous item analysis, 16 open-ended sentences and target words were chosen as the final set of items. The items in this section are all declarative present tense sentences consisting of a minimum of two and a maximum of five associations to the target word. Sentences either define the target word (definitional sentences = 62.5%) or contain vocabulary judged to be highly associated with the target word (associative sentences = 37.5%). Both sentence types provide naming clues that have been judged to aid word finding (Tulving, 1974; Wiig & Semel, 1984). The *definitional* sentences provide salient characteristics of the target word such as function, location, or perceptual attributes, while the *associative* sentences contain vocabulary frequently paired with the target word to aid the naming process. Of the definitional sentences, 50% contain a functional cue only, 10% contain both a functional and a locative cue, 10% contain a perceptual and a functional cue, and 30% contain a perceptual and a locative cue.

The implied target words were drawn from four sources: The *Ginn Intermediate Dictionary* (Morris, 1974), the *Macmillan Dictionary for Children* (Halsey & Morris, 1977), and vocabulary lists from first- through sixth-grade *Ginn Basal Readers* (Johnson et al., 1979) and first- through sixth-grade core and additional reading lists presented by Harris and Jacobson (1972).

Vocabulary selection was structured according to syntax, target-word frequency, and syllabication. With respect to the target-word selection criteria, the target words are distributed as follows: syntax, nouns = 100%; target-word frequency, low-frequency words = 63%, mid-frequency words = 12%, high-frequency words = 25% (Thorndike count of 120 juvenile books [Thorndike & Lorge, 1944]); and syllabication, monosyllabic words = 50%, two-syllable words = 25%, and three-syllable words = 25%.

DESCRIPTION NAMING

The Description Naming section is designed to assess naming accuracy (standard scores and percentile ranks) through an intrasensory auditory synthesis task which requires the subject to name a target word implied by three attributes. Naming tasks of this nature have been used to identify students with word-finding problems (German, 1979, 1984) and reading disorders (Rudel et al., 1981), as well as adults with naming disorders (Barton et al., 1969; Goodglass & Stuss, 1979; Luria, 1980). Initially, the Description Naming section consisted of 46 items. After rigorous item analysis, 12 sentences were selected as the final set of items. All descriptions were *wh*-questions defining the target word, using two to four salient attributes. Each description includes a category word (33%) or functional attribute (17%) or both (50%) and one to three of the following features identified as the most salient attributes of the target word: composition (50%), location (92%), size (42%), or sound (8%). Definitions were drawn from the *Ginn Intermediate Dictionary* (Morris, 1974), and implied target words were drawn from four sources: the *Ginn Intermediate Dictionary,* the *Macmillan Dictionary for Children* (Halsey & Morris, 1977), and vocabulary lists from the first- through sixth-grade *Ginn Basal Readers* (Johnson et al., 1979) and first- through sixth-grade core and additional reading lists presented by Harris and Jacobson (1972).

Vocabulary selection for this stimulus context was structured according to syntax, target-word frequency, and syllabication. Target words are represented as follows: syntax, nouns = 100%; target-word frequency, low-frequency words = 70%, mid-frequency words = 20%, high frequency words = 10% (Thorndike count of 120 juvenile books [Thorndike & Lorge, 1944]); and syllabication, monosyllabic words = 25%, two-syllable words = 58.3%, three-syllable words = 8.3%, and four-syllable words = 8.3%.

PICTURE NAMING: VERBS

The Picture Naming: Verbs section is designed to assess accuracy (standard scores and percentile ranks) in naming action target words. The subject is asked to label the action portrayed in the picture. Naming actions presented in a picture format has been employed to assess word-finding skills in adult aphasics

(Goodglass et al., 1966). Originally this section consisted of 71 target verbs in the present participle form, drawn from four sources: The *Ginn Intermediate Dictionary* (Morris, 1974), the *Macmillan Dictionary for Children* (Halsey & Morris, 1977), and vocabulary lists from the first- through sixth-grade *Ginn Basal Readers* (Johnson et al., 1979) and first- through sixth-grade core and additional reading lists presented by Harris and Jacobson (1972). After rigorous item analyses, 21 target words were chosen as the final set of items.

Vocabulary selection was structured according to four variables identified through clinical observations and research as influencing word-finding skills: syntax, picturability, target-word frequency, and syllabication. The vocabulary selection variables are distributed as follows: syntax, verbs = 100%; target-word frequency, low-frequency words = 66%, mid-frequency words = 5%, high-frequency words = 29% (frequency of occurrence in third- through ninth-grade reading texts reported in *American Heritage Word Frequency Book* [Carroll et al., 1971]); and syllabication, two-syllable words = 81%, three-syllable words = 9.5%, and four syllable words = 9.5%.

CATEGORY NAMING

Category Naming is designed to assess accuracy (standard scores and percentile ranks) in naming category words. Specifically, the subject is asked to name the implied category word for three subordinate or basic object-level words read by the examiner. Words representing objects at the basic object level have been identified experimentally as having the following characteristics in common: (a) attributes, (b) motor movements, (c) object similarity in shape, and (d) being identifiable by average shapes (Rosch, 1977; Rosch et al., 1976). Basic object-level words are contrasted with superordinate terms (e.g., the difference between "trout" and "fish," "sparrow" and "bird," "chair" and "furniture"). Basic objects have been shown to influence imagery, the perception of categories, naming practices, and perhaps even language structure.

Research in adult aphasia has investigated aphasics' ability to name instances of superordinate terms. Further, Luria (1980) recommended category-naming tasks in assessing word-finding skills in adult aphasics in order to determine disturbances of the "nominative function at a high level" (p. 514). Initially, this stimulus context consisted of 60 target words, each represented by three exemplars. Following rigorous item analyses, 21 category words were selected as the final set of items. Target words and their category members (exemplars) were drawn from six sources: Rosch's (1975) word lists of semantic categories and basic object-level members, Battig and Montague's (1969) category norms for verbal items in 56 categories, the *Ginn Intermediate Dictionary* (Morris, 1974), the *Macmillan Dictionary for Children* (Halsey & Morris, 1977), and vocabulary lists from first- through sixth-grade *Ginn Basal Readers* (Johnson et al., 1979) and first- through sixth-grade core and additional reading lists presented by Harris and Jacobson (1972).

Vocabulary selection was based on variables identified in current research on prototypicality and through clinical observations and research as influencing word-finding skills. Identified variables included syntax, target-word frequency, taxonomic level, and syllabication. Representation of the vocabulary selection variables is as follows: syntax, nouns = 100%; target-word frequency, low-frequency words = 19%, mid-frequency words = 10%, high-frequency words = 71% (Thorndike count of 120 juvenile books [Thorndike & Lorge, 1944]); taxonomic level, basic object level = 71%, superordinate level = 29%; and syllabication, monosyllabic words = 9.5%, two-syllable words = 52.4%, three-syllable words = 23.8%, and four-syllable words = 14.3%.

COMPREHENSION ASSESSMENT

By definition, individuals with word-finding problems have difficulty naming target words in the presence of good comprehension of those words (Johnson & Myklebust, 1967; Wiig & Semel, 1984). Therefore, the purpose of the comprehension assessment in the TAWF is to check the subject's knowledge of the target words he or she is unable to name or names incorrectly. Information derived in this manner will aid the examiner in differentiating receptive versus expressive language difficulties on the TAWF. Target-word comprehension would be expected on erred items thought to represent problems in word finding. The evaluation is performed after the word-finding assessment. Comprehension tasks consist of pictures and sentences representing those target words on which the individual made errors. All tasks require a recognition response only.

CHAPTER THREE

TEST DEVELOPMENT AND STANDARDIZATION

This section of the technical manual describes the development of the National College of Education *Test of Adolescent/Adult Word Finding* (TAWF), including item selection and analysis, as well as the standardization program employed.

ITEM SELECTION

FIELD TESTING FOR ITEM SELECTION

The pool of items generated for each stimulus context contained at least three times as many items as needed for the final edition of the TAWF. The items in the five word-finding sections were administered to 330 students—300 normally learning (50 at each grade level from 7 through 12) and 30 with word-finding problems in those same grades. The normally learning students were randomly chosen from a group of 500 students residing in Racine, Wisconsin, and attending school in the Racine Unified School District. The students with word-finding problems were selected from suburban schools in the Chicago metropolitan area. The students in this sample, composed of approximately equal numbers of males and females, had parents whose educational level was classified as either high school, some college, or college graduate.

ITEM SCALING

The data gathered in the item-analysis investigation were analyzed using the Rasch Latent Trait model, employing procedures recommended by Wright (Wright & Masters, 1982; Wright & Stone, 1979). This test construction model was selected because it produces an instrument with a level of measurement generalization not typically generated by classic models of test construction. Specifically, the Rasch Latent Trait model of test construction produces tests that are purported to be both item free and sample free (Wright & Stone, 1979), thus resulting in "objective mental measurement" (Wright, 1967, cited in Hashway, 1978). That is, when test items are shown to fit the model, the measures derived from such a test are independent of the items used to assess an individual's ability, and interpretation of the Rasch ability measures is independent of the sample used to calibrate the test. These two properties are not typically associated with traditionally constructed tests. Traditional models of test construction often result in sample-dependent item statistics and item-dependent ability estimates (Hambleton, 1979). Therefore, measurement generalization from tests developed in the traditional model is limited.

The Rasch model estimates a single parameter, item difficulty, which is used to construct two scales, one describing the relative difficulty of a set of items and the other the relative ability of a set of persons. However, the term *item difficulty* is defined differently in the Rasch model than in the traditional test construction model. Rasch item difficulty is defined as that point on the continuum where the probability of passing an item is 0.5. In contrast, the traditional index of item difficulty refers to the percentage of subjects who respond correctly to an item. The Rasch procedures provide both item and person reliability estimates corresponding to item and person scales. *Item reliability estimates* indicate the extent to which responses to items fit the expectations of a measurement model. *Person reliability estimates* indicate the extent to which a person's performance on a test fits model expectations (Wright & Masters, 1982). Scores generated from Rasch analyses are logistic transformations of the raw score. Scores on the item scale are referred to as *item difficulty;* scores on the person scale are referred to as *person ability.*

For the Rasch model, both item and person measurements are evaluated by several goodness-of-fit statistics. A *fit mean square* is computed for each test item and for each person taking the test. The item–fit mean square assesses the degree to which responses to an item conform to the model's predictions for a given level of item difficulty. Similarly, the person–fit mean square indicates the extent to which a person's responses to the items agree with the model's predictions for a given ability level. To facilitate evaluation, these mean squares are usually transformed to standardized values that have a mean near zero and a standard deviation near one. Items (or persons) with standardized fit values greater than $+2$ or less than -2 are generally considered poor fits to the model. These poor fits reflect erratic response patterns.

Several goodness-of-fit statistics are available to evaluate the reliability of the total set of items composing the scale and of the sample of persons tested. These global measures are based on the item and person standard deviations and indicate the extent to which the items span the difficulty scale and the extent to which the test distinguishes persons of varying ability levels. Of these measures, the item separation reliability index and the person separation reliability index are most easily interpreted. The reliability index estimates the proportion of observed variance that is not attributable to measurement error and has a range of values from 0 to 1.

In this item development and item analysis phase, data from both the normally learning sample and the sample of students with word-finding problems were analyzed using the Rasch model. Both items and people that did not meet the criteria indicated above were deleted. Rasch analyses were performed again on the remaining items and people. This stepwise procedure was implemented until a final set of items was established that met the goodness-of-fit criterion indicated above. The reliability index for persons was .83; the reliability index for items was .95. The final set of 148 items for the item analysis phase was distributed across the five naming sections as follows:

Picture Naming: Nouns	44 Items
Sentence Completion Naming	22 Items
Description Naming	20 Items
Picture Naming: Verbs	33 Items
Category Naming	29 Items
Total	148 Items

REFINEMENT OF THE TAWF

Preliminary analysis of the 148-item test administered to the standardization sample indicated additional items to be removed. By definition, an analysis of word finding must use vocabulary items that the intended population can be expected to have in their receptive language. Therefore, the normal students' and adults' comprehension scores for the target words in each section played a major role in the selection of the final TAWF items. Analyses of the comprehension scores obtained on each item were reviewed by grade and by adult age levels. Only items that received a mean comprehension score of at least 95% by the standardization sample were included in the final TAWF. As a result, some items were deleted because of low comprehension scores. The tables in Appendix A report the comprehension level achieved for each item by grade and age levels. The mean comprehension score on the final TAWF items was 99%.

Last, final Rasch analyses were conducted on the scores of adolescents and adults in the standardization sample to identify any remaining items with poor fits. Items with standardized fit values greater than 2.0 or less than -2.0 were removed. As a result of these additional analyses of item comprehension and item fit, 107 items were identified as appropriate for assessing word-finding skills in seventh- through twelfth-grade students and adults 20 to 80 years of age.

To compare the refined TAWF to the standardization edition, a validity investigation was conducted. The refined TAWF was administered to 67 normal learning students in grades 7 through 12 and 31 adults ranging in age from 20 to 80 years. These 98 subjects were matched with subjects in the standardization sample for sex, race/ethnicity, and level of parent's or subject's education. TAWF accuracy scores (Rasch ability scores) were analyzed to compare performance across the two samples. Main effect for groups did not emerge (seventh grade matched standardization sample: mean = 2.68, SD = .73, seventh grade validity sample: mean = 2.51, SD = .57; eighth grade matched standardization sample: mean = 2.50, *SD* = .73, eighth grade validity sample: mean = 2.51, *SD* = .85; ninth grade matched standardization sample: mean = 2.50, *SD* = .87, ninth grade validity sample: mean = 2.24, *SD* = .45; tenth grade matched standardization sample: mean = 2.90, *SD* = .93, tenth grade validity sample: mean = 3.21, *SD* = 1.00; eleventh grade matched standardization sample: mean = 2.62, *SD* = .67, eleventh grade validity sample: mean = 3.13, *SD* = .74; twelfth grade matched standardization sample: mean = 2.81, *SD* = .52, twelfth grade validity sample: mean = 3.10, *SD* = .79; adult matched standardization sample: mean = 2.80, *SD* = 1.1, adult validity sample: mean = 2.80, *SD* = .87, $F(1,180) = 1.26$, $p > .05$), indicating that word-finding assessment using the refined TAWF is not significantly different from word-finding assessment using the standardization edition.

Final Rasch analyses on the refined TAWF indicated a reliability index for person fit of .80 (*SD* = .78) and a reliability index for item fit of .99 (*SD* = .95). Thus, the final TAWF meets the Rasch model goodness-of-fit criteria. The individual item difficulty and fit mean square statistics are presented for each item in Table 3-1.

3-1 Table 3-1

Item Difficulties, Standardized Fit Mean Squares, and Standard Errors of Measurement for the Final Selection of Items on the TAWF, Based on the Rasch Latent Trait Item Analysis

Item	Item Difficulty	Standardized Fit Mean Square	Standard Error of Measurement
1-1	−2.30	0.07	0.23
1-2	−1.40	0.09	0.15
1-3	−0.99	0.00	0.12
1-4	−0.88	0.02	0.12
1-5	−0.84	0.07	0.12
1-6	−0.80	0.05	0.11
1-7	−0.65	0.17	0.11
1-8	−0.63	0.26	0.11
1-9	−0.58	0.02	0.10
1-10	−0.41	0.64	0.10
1-11	−0.33	−0.32	0.09
1-12	−0.29	0.47	0.09
1-13	−0.17	0.46	0.09
1-14	−0.15	−0.49	0.09
1-15	−0.05	−0.09	0.08
1-16	−0.05	0.16	0.08
1-17	−0.03	−0.22	0.08
1-18	0.01	−0.30	0.08
1-19	0.03	0.11	0.08
1-20	0.11	−0.40	0.08
1-21	0.22	−0.49	0.08
1-22	0.22	0.29	0.08
1-23	0.26	−0.47	0.08
1-24	0.36	−0.44	0.07
1-25	0.38	−0.62	0.07

3-1 Table 3-1
(Continued)
Item Difficulties, Standardized
Fit Mean Squares, and
Standard Errors of
Measurement for the Final
Selection of Items on the
TAWF, Based on the Rasch
Latent Trait Item Analysis

Item	Item Difficulty	Standardized Fit Mean Square	Standard Error of Measurement
1-26	0.38	−0.46	0.07
1-27	0.53	−1.01	0.07
1-28	0.67	−0.54	0.07
1-29	0.82	−0.89	0.06
1-30	0.85	0.77	0.06
1-31	0.98	1.32	0.06
1-32	1.37	1.25	0.06
1-33	1.39	−0.48	0.06
1-34	1.44	0.08	0.06
1-35	1.54	0.07	0.06
1-36	1.78	−0.43	0.05
1-37	1.90	1.14	0.05
2-1	−1.56	−0.06	0.16
2-2	−1.34	−0.07	0.14
2-3	−0.59	0.04	0.10
2-4	−0.40	0.04	0.10
2-5	−0.29	0.05	0.09
2-6	−0.23	0.38	0.09
2-7	−0.06	−0.16	0.08
2-8	0.01	0.55	0.08
2-9	0.04	−0.85	0.08
2-10	0.11	1.05	0.08
2-11	0.14	0.00	0.08
2-12	0.18	−0.60	0.08
2-13	0.19	−0.37	0.08
2-14	0.23	−0.43	0.08
2-15	0.26	−0.73	0.08
2-16	0.75	0.50	0.07
3-1	−1.26	0.09	0.14
3-2	−0.96	0.22	0.12
3-3	−0.52	−0.47	0.10
3-4	−0.42	−0.40	0.10
3-5	−0.23	−0.34	0.09
3-6	−0.11	0.34	0.09
3-7	0.08	1.46	0.08
3-8	0.08	0.14	0.08
3-9	0.76	0.47	0.07
3-10	0.88	−0.27	0.06
3-11	1.14	1.02	0.06
3-12	1.36	−1.46	0.06
4-1	−2.82	0.10	0.29
4-2	−2.21	0.04	0.22
4-3	−1.24	0.33	0.14
4-4	−0.96	0.05	0.12
4-5	−0.88	0.03	0.12
4-6	−0.87	0.03	0.12
4-7	−0.37	−0.01	0.10
4-8	−0.33	−0.02	0.09
4-9	−0.30	0.43	0.09
4-10	−0.10	0.00	0.09

	Item	Item Difficulty	Standardized Fit Mean Square	Standard Error of Measurement
3-1 Table 3-1 (Continued) Item Difficulties, Standardized Fit Mean Squares, and Standard Errors of Measurement for the Final Selection of Items on the TAWF, Based on the Rasch Latent Trait Item Analysis	4-11	0.13	0.76	0.08
	4-12	0.22	0.18	0.08
	4-13	0.55	0.53	0.07
	4-14	0.78	1.88	0.06
	4-15	1.13	-1.39	0.06
	4-16	1.26	-0.03	0.06
	4-17	1.29	1.72	0.06
	4-18	1.43	1.94	0.06
	4-19	1.47	1.91	0.06
	4-20	1.62	1.99	0.05
	4-21	1.84	0.33	0.05
	5-1	-1.44	0.09	0.15
	5-2	-1.30	-0.11	0.14
	5-3	-1.28	0.02	0.14
	5-4	-1.24	0.21	0.14
	5-5	-1.18	0.05	0.13
	5-6	-1.03	-0.04	0.13
	5-7	-0.99	0.02	0.12
	5-8	-0.88	-0.08	0.12
	5-9	-0.73	-0.13	0.11
	5-10	-0.51	-0.59	0.10
	5-11	-0.38	0.04	0.10
	5-12	-0.36	-0.28	0.09
	5-13	0.09	-0.38	0.08
	5-14	0.13	-1.20	0.08
	5-15	0.15	-0.07	0.08
	5-16	0.44	0.71	0.07
	5-17	0.99	1.20	0.06
	5-18	1.08	-1.08	0.06
	5-19	1.09	0.00	0.06
	5-20	1.39	-1.68	0.06
	5-21	1.42	-0.27	0.06

NATIONAL STANDARDIZATION

SAMPLING PLAN

The national standardization of the *Test of Adolescent/Adult Word Finding* (TAWF) was conducted according to a standardization program designed by the author and implemented by the DLM coordinator for the TAWF standardization. A description of the standardization plan follows.

Site and Sample Selection

Twenty-one sites were selected for the national standardization program. Nine were identified as primary sites, while 12 served as secondary sites. Special education administrators, speech and language pathologists, and/or principals at each primary site helped coordinate the data collection. Coordinators at each primary site distributed parent permission forms to the students attending the participating schools. In addition to the consent for testing information, the completed parent permission forms provided the coordinators with the educational attainment level and occupation of the student's parents as well as the primary language spoken in the home.

All returned permission forms were reviewed by the on-site coordinators. Because individuals with learning disabilities, speech and language problems, and reading disorders have been identified as having word-finding problems, students participating in exceptional education programs (speech and language programs, learning disabilities programs, behavioral disorders programs, etc.) were excluded from the potential normal standardization sample. This procedure was implemented to ensure that the normative population participating in the standardization would not have word-finding disorders.

Coordinators at each primary site also identified adults who were willing to participate in the standardization program. Adults completed permission forms that provided the following personal information: educational attainment level, occupation, primary language spoken in the home, and any remarkable health history. Because adults with brain trauma, neurological disease, cardiovascular strokes, fluency disorders, or learning disabilities have been identified as having a higher than normal incidence of word-finding problems, adults indicating these problems were excluded from the normal standardization sample.

Fifteen hundred adolescents and 600 adults were tested. Adolescents and adults were assigned to cells representing the stratification variables under consideration (sex, grade, chronological age, race or ethnicity, socioeconomic level, geographic region, and community size). Final participants were randomly chosen from the group of adolescents and adults assigned to each cell. The percentage of adolescents and adults drawn from each cell was derived from the percentage figures reported in the 1980 census appropriate for the site under consideration (U.S. Bureau of the Census, 1980). A final total of 1200 adolescents and 553 adults composed the standardization sample.

Secondary sites were coordinated by speech and language pathologists. Parent and adult permission forms were obtained, and individuals were tested by local coordinators or other speech and language pathologists. Adolescents and adults tested from the secondary sites were assigned to appropriate stratification groupings. For inclusion in the standardization sample, subjects from the secondary sites were randomly chosen from each grouping and assigned to the appropriate stratification cells in the standardization sample.

Mechanics of the Standardization Program

The standardization program commenced in October 1986 and ended in July 1987. Examiners were trained in the administration of the TAWF using demonstrations by the TAWF standardization coordinator. Participants included speech and language pathologists, learning disability specialists, classroom teachers, psychologists, and students in training programs for special education, school psychology, and speech and language pathology.

The TAWF was individually administered to each subject in the standardization sample. Each subject's responses on Section 1, Picture Naming: Nouns were recorded on audio cassette. Following the testing session, the audio recordings were used to calculate, to one hundredth of a second, the response times for each of the items in Section 1, Picture Naming: Nouns.

DEMOGRAPHIC PROFILE OF SUBJECTS IN THE STANDARDIZATION SAMPLE

Normal Subjects

The demographic profiles of the subjects who participated in the national standardization of the TAWF are presented in Tables 3-2 through 3-6. The normal sample consisted of 1200 adolescents in grades 7 through 12 and 553 adults aged 20 to 80 years residing in 21 states. Population data from the 1980 U.S. census were employed to ensure adequate representation with respect to such stratification variables as sex, ethnicity or race, geographic region, and the educational level of the adult subjects or the parents of the adolescents tested. These variables are discussed below.

Representation by Sex

The sampling plan required that the distribution of males and females in the standardization sample be representative of the total U.S. population. This objective was met, as indicated in Table 3-2.

Representation by Grade/Age Groupings

The sampling plan specified that 200 adolescents be tested at each of six grade levels and that 150 adults be tested at each of three age groupings. Since the initial sample exceeded this number at each grade- and age-level grouping, grade- and age-level groups were ultimately reduced to the required number of subjects who best matched the 1980 U.S. census data on all stratification variables. As shown in Table 3-2, the final sample consisted of 1200 adolescents, equally distributed across grades 7 through 12, and 553 adults, 201 in the 20–39 group, 200 in the 40–59 group, and 152 in the 60–80 group.

Representation by Chronological Age

The standardization sample consists of 10 age groups with a mean of 175.3 subjects at each age group. Except for the 18–19 year age group (91 students),

3-2 Table 3-2
Representation of the
Standardization Sample by
Sex and Grade/Age

Grade/Age (in years-months)	Females		Males		Totals	
	N	%	N	%	N	%
Seventh	100	5.7	100	5.7	200	11.4
Eighth	103	5.9	97	5.5	200	11.4
Ninth	100	5.7	100	5.7	200	11.4
Tenth	103	5.9	97	5.5	200	11.4
Eleventh	96	5.5	104	5.9	200	11.4
Twelfth	106	6.0	94	5.4	200	11.4
20-0 to 39-11	84	4.8	117	6.7	201	11.5
40-0 to 59-11	117	6.7	83	4.7	200	11.4
60-0 to 80-0	104	5.9	48	2.7	152	8.7
Total Sample	913	52.1	840	47.9	1753	100.0
U.S. Population*		51.4		48.6		100.0

*U.S. population data are from the Bureau of the Census, reported in the General Population Characteristics, United States Summary, Series PC80-1-B, Table 43. Washington, DC: U.S. Government Printing Office, 1980.
Note: Percentage totals do not always match or total 100% due to rounding.

more than 100 adolescents were included at each age level. As shown in Table 3-3, subjects ranged in age from 12 years 0 months to 80 years 0 months.

Representation by Geographic Region

Subjects in the standardization sample resided in 21 states, representing the four geographic regions defined in the 1980 census—Northeast, North Central, South, and West. As shown in Table 3-4, the distribution of the sample across the four regions closely matches the distribution figures reported in the 1980 census.

3-3 Table 3-3
Representation of the
Standardization Sample by
Sex and Age

Age (in years-months)	Females		Males		Total	
	N	%	N	%	N	%
12-0 to 12-11	63	3.6	54	3.1	117	6.7
13-0 to 13-11	99	5.6	107	6.1	206	11.8
14-0 to 14-11	92	5.2	90	5.1	182	10.4
15-0 to 15-11	109	6.2	92	5.2	201	11.5
16-0 to 16-11	98	5.6	102	5.8	200	11.4
17-0 to 17-11	108	6.2	95	5.4	203	11.6
18-0 to 19-11	39	2.2	52	3.0	91	5.2
20-0 to 39-11	84	4.8	117	6.7	201	11.5
40-0 to 59-11	117	6.7	83	4.7	200	11.4
60-0 to 80-0	104	5.9	48	2.7	152	8.7
TAWF Sample	913	52.1	840	47.9	1753	100.0

Note: Percentage totals do not always match or total 100% due to rounding.

3-4 Table 3-4
Representation of the Standardization Sample by Geographic Region and Grade/Age

Grade/Age (in years-months)	North Central		Northeast		South		West		Total	
	N	**%**	**N**	**%**	**N**	**%**	**N**	**%**	**N**	**%**
Seventh	48	2.7	39	2.2	78	4.4	35	2.0	200	11.4
Eighth	49	2.8	47	2.7	63	3.6	41	2.3	200	11.4
Ninth	52	3.0	46	2.6	69	3.9	33	1.9	200	11.4
Tenth	62	3.5	56	3.2	59	3.4	23	1.3	200	11.4
Eleventh	57	3.3	45	2.6	71	4.1	27	1.5	200	11.4
Twelfth	66	3.8	39	2.2	64	3.7	31	1.8	200	11.4
20-0 to 39-11	47	2.7	56	3.2	71	4.1	27	1.5	201	11.5
40-0 to 59-11	58	3.3	52	3.0	71	4.1	19	1.1	200	11.4
60-0 to 80-0	54	3.1	26	1.5	57	3.3	15	.9	152	8.7
Total Sample	493	28.1	406	23.2	603	34.4	251	14.3	1753	100.0
U.S. Population*		21.7		25.9		33.3		19.1		100.0

*U.S. population data are from the Bureau of the Census, U.S. Department of Commerce, reported in the 1980 Census of Population, PC80-81-1, Table 2. Washington, DC: US Government Printing Office, 1981. Note: Percentage totals do not always match or total 100% due to rounding.

Representation by Educational Level

Educational attainment has been used as an estimate of socioeconomic status (Kaufman & Kaufman, 1983). In order to ensure appropriate socioeconomic representation, the adolescents were divided according to their parents' level of educational attainment, and the adults were divided according to their own level of education. Three educational levels were considered, based on the number of school years completed: high school education or less (0 to 12 years), 3 years or less of college or technical training beyond high school (13 to 15 years), and college graduate or more (16 years or more). When number of years of schooling was reported for both parents, the parent with the highest educational attainment was used to categorize the adolescent. As shown in Table 3-5, the distribution of the standardization sample across educational levels approximates the distribution reported in the U.S. 1980 census.

Representation by Race or Ethnicity

Four ethnic or race categories were employed to ensure appropriate representation of race and/or ethnicity in the normative sample: white, black, Hispanic, and "other." The Hispanic population includes adolescents and adults of Mexican, Puerto Rican, Cuban, and other Spanish heritage. The "other" category includes Eskimos, Native Americans, Asians, and Pacific Islanders. In order to eliminate the possible interference of dual language abilities with retrieval skills, only monolingual adolescents and adults with English as their primary language were included in the standardization sample. As shown in Table 3-6, the TAWF normative sample closely matches the U.S. 1980 census figures with respect to race and ethnic distribution. In addition, the overall

3-5 Table 3-5

Representation of the Standardization Sample by Educational Level and Grade/Age

| Grade/Age (in years-months) | Educational Level | | | | | | | |
| | High School or Less | | One to Three Years of College or Technical Training | | Four or More Years of College | | Total | |
	N	%	N	%	N	%	N	%
Seventh	114	6.5	40	2.3	46	2.6	200	11.4
Eighth	109	6.2	61	3.5	30	1.7	200	11.4
Ninth	118	6.7	43	2.5	39	2.2	200	11.4
Tenth	117	6.7	45	2.6	38	2.2	200	11.4
Eleventh	117	6.7	35	2.0	48	2.7	200	11.4
Twelfth	99	5.6	47	2.7	54	3.1	200	11.4
20-0 to 39-11	92	5.2	32	1.8	77	4.4	201	11.5
40-0 to 59-11	82	4.7	43	2.5	75	4.3	200	11.4
60-0 to 80-0	78	4.4	34	1.9	40	2.3	152	8.7
Total Sample	926	52.8	380	21.7	447	25.5	1753	100.0
U.S. Population*		62.0		20.0		18.0		100.0

*U.S. population data are for ages 20 to 54 from the Bureau of the Census, reported in the Current Population Reports, Series P-20, No. 356, Educational Attainment in the United States: March 1979 and 1978. Table 2. Washington, DC: U.S. Government Printing Office, 1980.
Note: Percentage totals may not match or total 100% due to rounding.

3-6 Table 3-6

Representation of the Standardization Sample by Race, Ethnicity, and Grade/Age

| Grade/Age (in years-months) | Minority Group | | | | | | | | | | | |
| | White | | Black | | Hispanic | | Other* | | Total Minorities | | Total | |
	N	%	N	%	N	%	N	%	N	%	N	%
Seventh	152	8.7	23	1.3	12	.7	13	.7	48	2.7	200	11.4
Eighth	162	9.2	19	1.1	8	.5	11	.6	38	2.2	200	11.4
Ninth	159	9.1	22	1.3	10	.6	9	.5	41	2.3	200	11.4
Tenth	163	9.3	26	1.5	9	.5	2	.1	37	2.1	200	11.4
Eleventh	166	9.5	17	1.0	11	.6	6	.3	34	1.9	200	11.4
Twelfth	161	9.2	16	.9	12	.7	11	.6	39	2.2	200	11.4
20-0 to 39-11	180	10.3	13	.7	3	.2	5	.3	21	1.2	201	11.5
40-0 to 59-11	180	10.3	12	.7	5	.3	3	.2	20	1.1	200	11.4
60-0 to 80-0	151	8.6	1	.1	0	.0	0	.0	1	.1	152	8.7
Total Sample	1474	84.1	149	8.5	70	4.0	60	3.4	279	15.9	1753	100.0
U.S. Population**		79.4		11.7		6.4		2.5		20.6		100.0

*"Other" includes Asians, Native Americans, Eskimos, and Pacific Islanders.
**U.S. population data are from the Bureau of the Census, U.S. Department of Commerce, reported in the 1980 Census of Population, PC80-81-1, Table 1. Washington, DC: U.S. Government Printing Office, 1981. Reported percentages have been adjusted by data in the 1980 Census of Population PC80-81-1, indicating that 40% of Spanish origin persons reported their race as "other," whereas 56% reported their race as white.
Note: Percentage totals may not match or total 100% due to rounding.

percentage of total minorities in the normative sample closely approximates the percentages reported in the 1980 U.S. census.

Students with Word-Finding Problems

Representation by Linguistic Handicap

Because the purpose of the TAWF is to assess word-finding skills, adolescents with word-finding problems were included in the item analysis sample for item selection and in the standardization sample for item refinement of the TAWF. Therefore, linguistic handicap, defined as problems in word finding, was employed as a stratification variable to ensure inclusion of students with word-finding problems in the development of the TAWF. Participants with linguistic handicaps represented 3% (36 adolescents) of the number of normally learning adolescents in the standardization sample (these 36 subjects were not used in computing norms). These adolescents were randomly chosen from the pool of adolescents with word-finding problems identified for the TAWF validity studies. (See Chapter 5, Validity, for a description of procedures used to identify the population.) Distribution of the subjects across grade levels was as follows: 7 in grade 7, 6 in grade 8, 6 in grade 9, 6 in grade 10, 8 in grade 11, and 3 in grade 12. Table 3-7 delineates the demographic characteristics of the special sample as percentages of the combined linguistically handicapped and normal subjects in the standardization samples. Table 3-8 presents the demographic profile of the adolescents with word-finding problems included in the standardization sample. Throughout this manual, where appropriate, parallel findings are reported for adolescents with word-finding problems.

Representation by Community Size

Subjects in the standardization sample were drawn from three types of communities: 45% resided in a suburb or small town (population 2500 to

3-7 Table 3-7
Representation of the Linguistically Handicapped Population (*N* = 36) in the Standardization Sample (*N* = 1236)

Sex		Region			Parent Educational Level			Ethnicity or Race			
M	F	NC	W	S	1	2	3	W	B	H	O
4%	2%	4%	2%	5%	4%	2%	2%	3%	5%	3%	0%

3-8 Table 3-8
Demographic Profile of the Standardization Participants with Word-Finding Problems (*N* = 36)

Sex		Region			Parent Educational Level			Ethnicity or Race			
M	F	NC	W	S	1	2	3	W	B	H	O
72%	28%	33.3%	8.3%	58.3%	72%	14%	14%	75%	19%	6%	0%

49,999), 39% resided in a central city (population 50,000 or more), while 16% of the sample resided in rural areas.

A total of 21 communities participated in the national TAWF standardization. Two primary sites and two to seven secondary sites were selected from each of the four regions derived from the 1980 census. Primary sites were those locations where the number of individuals tested exceeded 30; secondary sites were those locations in which the number of individuals participating was 30 or less. The geographic distribution of the 21 communities included in the national standardization is shown in Figure 3-1.

OVERALL PERFORMANCE BY STRATIFICATION VARIABLE

TAWF performance data were compared for selected subgroups of individuals representing key stratification variables in the standardization sample. Tables 3-9 through 3-12 report the mean TAWF accuracy raw scores for groups classified by these variables at each grade or age level. Table 3-9 reports scores by sex.

3-1 **Figure 3-1**

Communities participating in the TAWF national standardization program

3-9 Table 3-9
TAWF Mean Raw Scores and Standard Deviations by Sex for Grade/Age Groupings of the Normal Subjects in the Standardization Sample

Grade/Age (in years-months)	Females			Males		
	N	Mean	SD	N	Mean	SD
Seventh	100	89.3	8.9	100	88.0	8.8
Eighth	100	90.8	8.2	100	89.8	8.2
Ninth	100	92.4	9.1	100	93.7	7.0
Tenth	100	93.1	7.6	100	94.0	7.0
Eleventh	100	94.1	6.8	100	94.6	7.1
Twelfth	100	96.1	6.4	100	96.3	7.0
20-0 to 39-11	84	98.0	6.2	117	100.6	5.6
40-0 to 59-11	117	97.4	6.9	83	97.3	7.3
60-0 to 80-0	104	89.9	10.2	48	92.3	8.2

When all grades were combined, the difference in mean raw scores between adolescent females and adolescent males was .02. When all ages were combined, the difference between adult females and adult males was 2.92. The mean for males was higher for both adolescent and adult groups.

Table 3-10 reports scores by region. When all grades were combined, the difference in mean raw scores between adolescent groups by region ranged from .06 (North Central higher than West) to 2.53 (North Central higher than South). When all ages were combined, the difference between adult groups by region ranged from .60 (Northeast higher than West) to 3.74 (Northeast higher than South).

Table 3-11 reports scores by educational attainment level of adolescents' parents and educational attainment level of adults in the standardization sample. When all grades were combined, the difference in mean raw scores between adolescent groups by parents' educational attainment level ranged from .90 (those whose parents had some college or technical training were higher than those whose parents had high school or less) to 2.43 (those whose parents were

3-10 Table 3-10
TAWF Mean Raw Scores and Standard Deviations by Region for Grade/Age Groupings of the Normal Subjects in the Standardization Sample

Grade/Age (in years-months)	North Central			Northeast			South			West		
	N	Mean	SD	N	Mean	SD	N	Mean	SD	N	Mean	SD
Seventh	48	88.8	9.2	39	89.1	9.1	78	88.3	8.9	35	88.8	8.5
Eighth	49	92.0	7.3	47	88.9	7.6	63	89.4	9.2	41	91.4	8.0
Ninth	52	94.4	7.3	46	92.3	7.3	69	91.3	9.2	33	95.3	7.6
Tenth	61	95.0	6.5	56	92.3	7.8	60	92.8	7.3	23	94.5	6.7
Eleventh	57	94.5	7.4	45	93.3	7.3	71	93.6	6.6	27	97.7	5.4
Twelfth	66	98.1	5.9	39	94.0	6.9	64	94.6	7.2	31	98.6	5.2
20-0 to 39-11	47	100.3	5.2	56	99.5	5.6	71	98.1	7.1	27	101.3	3.9
40-0 to 59-11	58	97.2	7.1	52	100.1	4.4	71	95.5	8.1	19	97.6	6.7
60-0 to 80-0	54	91.3	10.3	26	92.3	7.7	57	89.1	10.3	15	91.5	7.0

3-11 Table 3-11

TAWF Mean Raw Scores and Standard Deviations by Educational Attainment Level for Grade/Age Groupings of the Normal Subjects in the Standardization Sample

Grade/Age (in years-months)	High School or Less			Some College or Technical Training			College Graduate		
	N	Mean	SD	N	Mean	SD	N	Mean	SD
Seventh	114	87.9	9.6	40	87.4	7.9	46	91.6	7.2
Eighth	109	90.7	8.1	61	89.4	8.6	30	90.7	7.8
Ninth	118	92.0	8.6	43	96.5	6.0	39	92.2	8.0
Tenth	117	93.2	7.3	45	94.1	7.2	38	93.8	6.8
Eleventh	117	92.8	7.3	35	95.1	5.8	48	97.5	5.7
Twelfth	99	95.0	7.3	47	97.2	6.1	54	97.6	5.5
20-0 to 39-11	92	97.6	6.4	32	98.9	5.9	77	101.8	4.5
40-0 to 59-11	82	94.7	7.6	43	96.1	7.2	75	101.0	4.1
60-0 to 80-0	78	89.8	10.1	34	88.6	8.6	40	94.0	8.7

college graduates were higher than those whose parents had high school or less). When all ages were combined, the difference between adult groups by educational attainment level ranged from .38 (adults with some college or technical training were higher than adults with high school or less) to 5.68 (adults who are college graduates were higher than adults with high school or less). The difference between adults with some college or technical training and adults who were college graduates was 5.30.

Table 3-12 reports scores by race/ethnicity. When all grades were combined, the difference in mean raw scores between adolescent groups by racial/ethnic background ranged from 1.56 (white higher than "other") to 6.28 (white higher than black). When all ages were combined, the difference between adults in the white and black groups was only 2.45. There were not sufficient numbers of adults in the Hispanic or "other" groups to make meaningful comparisons.

3-12 Table 3-12

TAWF Mean Raw Scores and Standard Deviations by Grade/Age Groupings and Race or Ethnicity of the Normal Subjects in the Standardization Sample

Grade/Age (in years-months)	White			Black			Hispanic			Other		
	N	Mean	SD	N	Mean	SD	N	Mean	SD	N	Mean	SD
Seventh	152	89.7	8.1	23	86.0	10.4	12	80.9	10.5	13	87.9	9.3
Eighth	162	91.3	7.9	19	84.8	7.3	8	87.6	6.2	11	88.1	10.0
Ninth	159	94.3	7.0	22	84.7	10.0	10	90.7	9.8	9	94.0	9.8
Tenth	163	94.4	6.3	26	88.9	9.6	9	87.8	7.6	2	102.5	.7
Eleventh	166	94.9	6.5	17	88.3	8.5	11	92.6	6.6	6	95.8	8.1
Twelfth	161	96.8	6.4	16	92.2	8.7	12	94.6	7.3	11	95.5	5.5
20-0 to 39-11	180	99.9	5.7	13	96.2	5.6	3	91.7	12.4	5	97.0	6.4
40-0 to 59-11	180	97.8	6.8	12	96.5	6.6	5	85.4	7.1	3	97.7	4.5
60-0 to 80-0	151	90.7	9.6	1	87.0	0.0	0	00.0	0.0	0	00.0	0.0

Interpretation of score differences between groups like those in Tables 3-9 through 3-12 should be done with caution because the differences do not take into account the interaction of variables used to construct the groups. For example, a difference between scores of two groups classified by racial/ethnic variables should not be considered without an understanding that some of the difference may be explained by the various educational attainment levels of the parents or individuals in the groups. The interaction of differences such as these cannot be effectively studied without pairing samples that have been carefully matched to each other by as many characteristics as the experimenter considers possibly relevant.

NORM DEVELOPMENT BY GRADE AND AGE LEVEL

Two types of derived scores are provided for both the complete TAWF and the Brief Test—standard scores and percentile ranks. (See the TAWF *Administration, Scoring and Interpretation Manual.)* These normative scores are provided for grade and age levels in the standardization sample. Three steps were used to obtain the norms.

1. As indicated in the item-analysis section, the TAWF was calibrated using the Rasch Latent Trait model, employing procedures suggested by Rasch and Wright (Wright & Stone, 1979). Through this procedure, logit scale scores were derived for the TAWF raw scores. All TAWF norms are based on the logit scale scores generated from the Rasch analysis. Although these logit scale scores may be used as units of comparison, they contain two numerical characteristics that make them confusing—decimals and negatives (Wright & Stone, 1979). Therefore, the logit scale scores for each grade and age level were transformed to z scores. The resulting z scores were then converted to standard scores by grade and age level.

2. Next, for both the complete TAWF and the TAWF Brief Test, z scores were converted to standard scores with a mean of 100 and a standard deviation of 15 by employing the following formula:

$$SS = M + (SD)(z),$$

where the standard score *(SS)* equals the mean *(M)* of the distribution of standard scores added to the product of the standard deviation *(SD)* of the distribution of standard scores times the z score. Norm tables are presented in the TAWF *Administration, Scoring and Interpretation Manual.*

   Thus, standard scores for both the complete TAWF and the TAWF Brief Test have a mean equal to 100 and a standard deviation of 15. Because the standard score norms for both versions are based on the same sample and use the same mean and standard deviation, examiners can directly compare scores obtained for a subject on the two versions of the test.

3. Percentile ranks were computed for each age and grade level from frequencies of obtained logit ability scores and have been smoothed slightly at the tails of each distribution in order to adjust for minor sampling irregularities.

TIME INDEX

The TAWF provides the examiner with two procedures for assessing a subject's response latencies: the optional Average Item Response Time measurement and the Estimated Item Response Time procedure. The optional Average Item Response Time index is based on the measurement, determined from a tape recording of Section 1 of the complete TAWF, of the interval between the presentation of each picture and the subject's response to that item. This procedure is used to determine a subject's speed in naming. Tables 3-13 and 3-14 present the Average Item Response Times and standard deviations for Section 1 by grade and age for the normally learning students and adults. Tables 3-15, 3-16, and 3-17 present the mean response times and standard deviation for each item in Section 1, by grade and age for the normally learning students, and by age for normal adults.

The Estimated Item Response Time procedure is a judgment of whether the response delays for items in Section 1 of either the complete TAWF or the TAWF Brief Test are greater than or less than 4 seconds. With this procedure, examiners can evaluate an individual's speed in naming during test administration. Table 3-18 presents the number of response delays (4 seconds

3-13 Table 3-13

TAWF Average Item Response Times and Standard Deviations for Section 1 by Normal Students in the Standardization Sample in Grades 7 through 12

Grade	N	Average Item Response Time	
		Mean	*SD*
Seventh	190	1.72	.61
Eighth	191	1.63	.59
Ninth	190	1.55	.51
Tenth	188	1.57	.54
Eleventh	190	1.50	.49
Twelfth	165	1.47	.53

3-14 Table 3-14

TAWF Average Item Response Times and Standard Deviations for Section 1 by Normal Adults in the Standardization Sample in Three Age Groups, 20 through 80 Years

Age (in years-months)	N	Average Item Response Time	
		Mean	*SD*
20-0 to 39-11	161	1.39	.50
40-0 to 59-11	161	1.68	.57
60-0 to 80-0	127	2.11	.87

3-15 Table 3-15

TAWF Mean Item Response Times and Standard Deviations of Items in Section 1 for Normal Students in the Standardization Sample by Ages 12-0 to 18-11

	Age Groups (in years-months)								
	12-0 to 12-11			13-0 to 13-11			14-0 to 14-11		
Item	Mean	SD	N	Mean	SD	N	Mean	SD	N
1	.79	.46	111	.79	.30	194	.77	.25	174
2	1.02	.35	111	1.02	.56	196	1.10	.84	173
3	1.92	2.33	111	1.55	1.58	196	1.54	1.82	174
4	1.23	.73	111	1.20	.55	196	1.47	1.71	174
5	1.41	1.81	111	1.58	2.21	196	1.65	2.37	174
6	1.49	2.03	111	1.26	1.38	196	1.32	1.74	174
7	.91	.29	111	.99	.83	196	.99	.69	174
8	1.16	.92	111	1.06	.45	196	1.07	.54	173
9	1.18	.66	111	1.21	.72	195	1.14	.68	174
10	1.18	1.08	110	1.26	.86	193	1.21	.87	173
11	1.47	1.91	111	1.29	1.00	196	1.23	.96	174
12	1.80	2.02	111	1.69	1.43	195	1.62	1.29	174
13	.98	.33	111	.91	.36	195	.95	.36	174
14	2.14	2.94	111	2.33	3.44	195	1.89	2.72	173
15	1.33	1.52	110	1.60	2.24	196	1.24	1.45	172
16	1.37	1.66	111	1.29	.99	196	1.28	.96	173
17	1.21	1.42	111	1.34	1.44	196	1.19	.88	174
18	1.35	1.31	111	1.41	1.32	196	1.37	1.59	174
19	1.07	.58	111	1.18	.79	196	1.25	1.45	173
20	1.66	1.49	111	1.46	.82	196	1.44	.83	173
21	1.12	1.61	110	1.10	.57	196	1.15	.83	174
22	1.07	.56	111	1.13	.72	196	1.02	.45	174
23	1.53	1.72	111	1.50	1.62	196	1.38	1.72	174
24	1.85	1.65	111	2.00	1.73	195	1.85	1.84	173
25	2.12	2.52	110	1.54	1.52	196	1.61	1.23	173
26	2.52	2.70	111	2.37	3.12	194	2.27	2.66	174
27	2.06	2.56	110	1.73	1.47	195	1.92	2.35	173
28	2.07	2.94	111	1.94	2.05	195	1.92	1.90	173
29	2.51	2.98	111	2.54	2.98	195	2.19	2.59	174
30	1.90	2.23	111	1.78	2.05	196	1.64	1.75	174
31	2.42	2.59	111	2.53	2.88	196	2.85	3.02	173
32	2.38	2.31	110	2.54	2.81	195	2.62	2.84	173
33	2.59	2.99	111	2.67	2.67	196	2.57	2.83	174
34	2.19	2.61	111	2.30	2.62	195	1.94	1.87	174
35	2.68	2.98	111	2.64	2.82	196	2.44	2.68	171
36	2.79	3.04	111	2.97	3.04	196	2.17	1.89	173
37	2.28	2.63	111	2.01	1.62	196	2.12	2.07	174
Average Item Response Time									
	1.70	.63	111	1.67	.56	196	1.60	.57	174

or longer) for each grade-level grouping for both the complete TAWF and the Brief Test. Table 3-19 presents the number of response delays (4 seconds or longer) for each age-level grouping. These numbers represent the maximum number of response delays (4 seconds or longer) on both the complete TAWF and the Brief Test exhibited by 80% of the individuals in each indicated grade- and age-level grouping.

3-15 Table 3-15
(Continued)
TAWF Mean Item Response
Times and Standard
Deviations of Items in Section
1 for Normal Students in the
Standardization Sample by
Ages 12-0 to 18-11

Item	Age Groups (in years-months)								
	15-0 to 15-11			16-0 to 16-11			17-0 to 17-11		
	Mean	*SD*	*N*	*Mean*	*SD*	*N*	*Mean*	*SD*	*N*
1	.76	.31	192	.74	.20	185	.75	.28	187
2	.96	.36	193	1.06	.66	185	.95	.40	188
3	1.47	1.76	193	1.31	1.14	185	1.48	1.54	188
4	1.31	1.04	193	1.25	.85	185	1.19	.61	188
5	1.20	1.18	193	1.31	1.67	185	1.56	2.10	187
6	1.12	.82	193	1.13	.94	185	1.17	1.33	188
7	.88	.42	193	.87	.32	183	.93	.53	188
8	1.02	.59	193	1.96	.35	184	1.01	.75	188
9	1.08	.69	192	1.10	.73	184	1.11	1.19	188
10	1.19	1.01	193	1.20	1.18	184	1.09	.84	188
11	1.21	.89	193	1.18	.82	185	1.18	1.12	188
12	1.70	1.82	193	1.64	1.49	185	1.59	1.41	188
13	.87	.28	192	.91	.36	183	.87	.25	188
14	1.78	2.06	193	1.65	2.01	184	1.85	2.16	188
15	1.23	1.33	192	1.20	1.11	185	1.05	.52	188
16	1.20	.91	193	1.18	.71	185	1.22	.92	188
17	1.16	.97	193	1.17	1.12	185	1.30	1.70	188
18	1.41	1.72	193	1.23	1.04	185	1.43	1.59	188
19	1.17	1.27	193	1.09	.74	183	1.14	.68	188
20	1.47	1.25	193	1.37	.84	184	1.27	.71	188
21	1.14	.84	193	1.05	.56	185	1.04	.61	188
22	1.03	.47	193	1.07	.67	185	1.12	1.17	188
23	1.47	1.66	192	1.46	1.83	185	1.52	1.78	186
24	1.66	1.01	192	1.82	1.51	185	1.63	1.48	188
25	1.94	2.13	193	1.70	1.77	185	1.79	2.38	188
26	1.84	2.06	193	1.73	1.88	185	1.79	1.98	188
27	1.59	1.59	193	1.61	1.55	182	1.82	2.17	188
28	2.16	2.78	193	1.97	2.41	185	2.17	2.59	188
29	1.89	2.31	193	2.05	2.02	184	1.87	2.21	188
30	1.42	1.17	193	1.48	1.58	184	1.50	1.29	187
31	2.32	2.51	193	2.20	2.33	184	2.21	2.37	188
32	2.34	2.30	193	2.62	2.45	183	2.57	2.70	188
33	2.52	2.85	193	2.73	2.86	183	2.80	2.94	186
34	1.85	1.60	193	1.81	1.47	184	1.75	1.90	188
35	2.62	2.93	191	2.42	2.84	184	2.38	2.67	187
36	2.20	1.95	192	2.53	2.81	185	2.27	2.21	188
37	2.47	2.71	193	2.47	2.16	185	2.23	1.90	188
Average Item Response Time									
	1.53	.53	193	1.52	.48	185	1.53	.60	188

3-15 **Table 3-15**
(Continued)
TAWF Mean Item Response Times and Standard Deviations of Items in Section 1 for Normal Students in the Standardization Sample by Ages 12-0 to 18-11

| | Age Group | | |
| | 18-0 to 18-11 | | |
Item	Mean	SD	N
1	.76	.35	67
2	1.10	.70	67
3	1.95	2.46	67
4	1.18	.71	67
5	1.62	1.93	66
6	1.05	.49	67
7	.82	.35	67
8	.97	.45	66
9	1.07	.45	67
10	1.34	1.28	67
11	1.40	1.94	67
12	1.65	1.79	67
13	.91	.33	67
14	1.63	2.03	67
15	1.17	.94	67
16	1.30	.81	67
17	1.31	1.03	67
18	1.50	2.29	67
19	1.17	.84	67
20	1.21	.56	67
21	1.06	.74	67
22	1.02	.56	67
23	1.56	2.21	67
24	1.51	.89	67
25	1.73	1.89	67
26	1.68	1.82	67
27	1.81	2.05	67
28	2.28	2.78	67
29	2.17	2.79	67
30	1.99	2.54	67
31	3.21	3.59	67
32	2.39	2.33	66
33	2.27	2.13	67
34	1.98	2.40	67
35	2.07	2.26	67
36	2.19	1.82	67
37	2.19	2.05	67
Average Item Response Time			
	1.57	.51	67

3-16 Table 3-16

TAWF Mean Item Response Times and Standard Deviations of Items in Section 1 for Normal Students in the Standardization Sample by Grades 7 through 12

Item	Grade 7 Mean	SD	N	Grade 8 Mean	SD	N	Grade 9 Mean	SD	N
1	.80	.41	179	.76	.23	180	.78	.34	177
2	1.04	.54	179	1.04	.65	180	.97	.39	177
3	1.89	2.29	179	1.42	1.08	180	1.46	1.65	177
4	1.21	.67	179	1.41	1.33	180	1.37	1.41	177
5	1.50	1.82	179	1.66	2.47	180	1.32	1.43	177
6	1.58	2.36	179	1.23	1.15	180	1.18	1.08	177
7	.99	.85	179	.96	.62	180	.95	.50	177
8	1.14	.80	179	1.08	.55	180	1.02	.52	177
9	1.21	.68	179	1.18	.78	180	1.10	.71	177
10	1.27	1.01	179	1.16	.88	180	1.22	1.08	177
11	1.39	1.54	179	1.22	.91	180	1.22	1.01	177
12	1.74	1.76	179	1.73	1.66	180	1.58	1.31	177
13	.98	.34	179	.91	.35	180	.91	.36	177
14	2.47	3.50	179	1.83	2.60	180	1.90	2.58	177
15	1.46	1.86	179	1.49	2.13	180	1.25	1.49	177
16	1.43	1.56	179	1.24	.74	180	1.23	1.05	177
17	1.30	1.56	179	1.34	1.25	180	1.15	.94	177
18	1.47	1.64	179	1.46	1.55	180	1.32	1.39	177
19	1.13	.69	179	1.17	1.25	180	1.25	1.35	177
20	1.58	1.58	179	1.51	1.01	180	1.39	.74	177
21	1.09	.58	179	1.12	.59	180	1.22	1.06	177
22	1.07	.53	179	1.07	.71	180	1.03	.57	177
23	1.71	2.21	179	1.42	1.48	180	1.34	1.39	177
24	1.98	1.71	179	1.97	1.85	180	1.77	1.51	177
25	1.96	2.35	179	1.59	1.40	180	1.79	1.81	177
26	2.50	2.87	179	2.28	2.94	180	2.17	2.60	177
27	2.11	2.34	179	1.81	2.09	180	1.44	.97	177
28	2.04	2.59	179	2.01	2.39	180	2.04	2.34	177
29	2.80	3.22	179	2.19	2.64	180	2.29	2.78	177
30	1.92	2.29	179	1.68	1.86	180	1.53	1.27	177
31	2.40	2.80	179	2.65	2.93	180	2.59	2.65	177
32	2.41	2.44	179	2.62	2.95	180	2.69	2.88	177
33	2.84	3.28	179	2.52	2.52	180	2.39	2.63	177
34	2.34	2.85	179	2.14	2.35	180	1.70	1.34	177
35	2.77	3.12	179	2.62	2.81	180	2.44	2.57	177
36	2.96	3.22	179	2.73	2.67	180	2.24	1.93	177
37	2.09	2.29	179	2.06	1.86	180	2.44	2.31	177
Average Item Response Time									
	1.72	.61	179	1.63	.59	180	1.55	.51	177

3-16 Table 3-16
(Continued)
TAWF Mean Item Response
Times and Standard
Deviations of Items in Section
1 for Normal Students in the
Standardization Sample by
Grades 7 through 12

Item	Grade 10			Grade 11			Grade 12		
	Mean	*SD*	*N*	*Mean*	*SD*	*N*	*Mean*	*SD*	*N*
1	.75	.27	178	.76	.25	180	.74	.30	156
2	1.06	.78	178	.99	.55	180	.99	.51	156
3	1.51	1.70	178	1.37	1.36	180	1.56	1.86	156
4	1.25	.77	178	1.19	.55	180	1.14	.63	156
5	1.25	1.29	178	1.38	1.90	180	1.70	2.28	156
6	1.19	1.34	178	1.16	.96	180	.97	.52	156
7	.89	.38	178	.94	.52	180	.81	.29	156
8	1.01	.46	178	1.01	.76	180	.93	.31	156
9	1.11	.75	178	1.13	1.14	180	1.04	.66	156
10	1.25	1.23	178	1.12	.73	180	1.12	.93	156
11	1.24	.85	178	1.16	.80	180	1.24	1.67	156
12	1.85	2.00	178	1.55	1.32	180	1.56	1.48	156
13	.90	.31	178	.88	.30	180	.86	.26	156
14	1.79	2.07	178	1.73	2.18	180	1.64	2.06	156
15	1.20	.91	178	1.14	1.01	180	1.07	.72	156
16	1.23	.84	178	1.17	.74	180	1.13	.65	156
17	1.21	1.30	178	1.19	1.35	180	1.18	1.04	156
18	1.36	1.43	178	1.28	1.10	180	1.45	2.10	156
19	1.07	.67	178	1.08	.71	180	1.13	.70	156
20	1.41	1.25	178	1.34	.76	180	1.19	.65	156
21	1.08	.54	178	1.13	.79	180	.95	.38	156
22	1.12	1.13	178	1.18	.80	180	.91	.34	156
23	1.56	1.99	178	1.45	1.79	180	1.38	1.62	156
24	1.68	1.18	178	1.74	1.50	180	1.51	1.17	156
25	1.90	2.14	178	1.59	1.51	180	1.55	2.04	156
26	1.90	2.27	178	1.70	1.61	180	1.65	1.90	156
27	1.76	2.01	178	1.68	1.58	180	1.70	2.00	156
28	2.19	2.83	178	2.04	2.38	180	1.97	2.41	156
29	1.91	2.12	178	1.83	1.64	180	1.92	2.55	156
30	1.48	1.32	178	1.54	1.49	180	1.47	1.61	156
31	2.22	2.58	178	2.29	2.36	180	2.56	3.01	156
32	2.54	2.76	178	2.49	2.03	180	2.38	2.45	156
33	2.55	2.74	178	2.90	2.93	180	2.52	2.82	156
34	2.02	1.91	178	1.87	1.84	180	1.65	1.76	156
35	2.75	3.10	178	2.32	2.67	180	2.08	2.17	156
36	2.52	2.73	178	2.20	2.13	180	2.17	1.95	156
37	2.45	2.63	178	2.38	2.09	180	2.11	1.81	156
Average Item Response Time									
	1.57	.54	178	1.50	.49	180	1.47	.53	156

3-17 Table 3-17

TAWF Mean Item Response Times and Standard Deviations of Items in Section 1 for Normal Adults in the Standardization Sample by Ages 20-0 to 80-0

	Age Groups (in years-months)								
	20-0 to 39-11			**40-0 to 59-11**			**60-0 to 80-0**		
Item	**Mean**	**SD**	**N**	**Mean**	**SD**	**N**	**Mean**	**SD**	**N**
1	.90	.49	158	.86	.37	160	1.10	1.35	127
2	1.01	.44	161	1.05	.69	161	1.65	1.56	127
3	1.17	.94	161	1.33	1.07	161	1.66	1.72	127
4	1.17	.60	161	1.55	1.08	161	2.15	2.20	127
5	1.17	1.24	160	1.58	2.36	161	1.54	2.34	127
6	1.30	1.61	160	.99	.50	161	1.09	.72	127
7	1.05	.62	161	1.63	1.67	161	2.79	2.85	127
8	1.00	.44	161	1.14	.53	161	1.36	1.05	127
9	1.29	.78	160	1.61	1.50	160	1.90	1.95	127
10	1.69	1.75	156	2.06	2.21	159	2.17	2.00	126
11	1.26	2.06	160	1.40	1.25	161	2.29	2.44	126
12	1.72	1.08	161	2.12	1.53	161	2.69	2.59	127
13	.95	.39	161	1.07	.54	161	1.23	.68	127
14	1.34	1.45	161	1.69	1.71	161	3.01	3.56	126
15	1.00	.44	160	1.33	.98	161	1.97	1.86	127
16	1.22	.77	161	1.60	1.25	161	1.75	1.81	127
17	1.01	.61	159	1.15	.89	161	1.37	1.67	127
18	1.20	.76	160	1.49	1.48	161	1.81	1.85	127
19	1.31	1.19	160	1.73	1.66	161	2.45	2.68	126
20	1.40	.76	160	1.56	1.04	161	2.48	2.11	127
21	1.17	1.08	161	1.75	1.43	159	2.54	1.95	127
22	1.58	2.28	161	2.17	2.23	160	2.73	2.20	126
23	1.27	1.39	161	1.40	1.62	161	1.49	1.55	127
24	1.31	.60	160	1.50	.90	160	1.95	1.67	125
25	1.28	1.00	160	1.34	1.31	161	2.15	2.71	126
26	1.42	1.57	160	1.60	1.95	160	2.30	2.65	126
27	1.38	1.22	161	1.34	1.46	161	1.32	.78	127
28	1.78	1.89	161	2.65	3.32	160	3.42	3.68	127
29	1.34	1.07	161	1.58	1.90	161	1.68	1.92	127
30	1.26	1.54	161	1.21	1.03	160	1.08	.79	127
31	1.71	2.02	161	1.86	2.16	161	1.97	2.25	127
32	2.64	2.13	161	3.35	3.01	160	4.69	3.71	127
33	2.23	2.14	161	2.80	2.53	159	2.56	2.78	127
34	1.53	1.60	161	1.78	2.17	161	1.99	1.58	127
35	2.01	2.33	161	2.78	3.10	161	2.28	2.35	127
36	1.62	1.09	161	1.94	2.07	161	2.65	2.96	127
37	2.03	1.87	161	2.56	2.48	161	3.08	2.70	127
Average Item Response Time									
	1.39	.71	161	1.68	.57	161	2.11	.87	127

3-18 Table 3-18

Maximum Number of Response Delays (4 Seconds or Longer) Exhibited by 80% of the Standardization Sample for the Complete TAWF and the TAWF Brief Test on Section 1, Picture Naming: Nouns, by Grade-Level Groupings

Grade	Complete	Brief Test
Seventh	5	2
Eighth	5	2
Ninth	4	2
Tenth	4	2
Eleventh	4	2
Twelfth	4	2

3-19 Table 3-19

Maximum Number of Response Delays (4 Seconds or Longer) Exhibited by 80% of the Standardization Sample for the Complete TAWF and the TAWF Brief Test on Section 1, Picture Naming: Nouns, by Age-Level Groupings

Age (in months-years)	Complete Test	Brief Test
12-0 to 12-11	5	2
13-0 to 13-11	5	2
14-0 to 14-11	4	2
15-0 to 15-11	4	2
16-0 to 16-11	4	2
17-0 to 19-11	4	2
20-0 to 39-11	3	2
40-0 to 59-11	4	2
60-0 to 80-0	7	3

CHAPTER FOUR

RELIABILITY

As indicated in Chapter 3, the Rasch calibration and scaling procedures provide both item and person reliability estimates. TAWF reliability estimates were based on the Rasch Latent Trait model, but traditional reliability assessments are also reported for comparison purposes.

ITEM SCALE RELIABILITY

With latent trait models, the analog of traditional reliability estimates is the goodness-of-fit statistic. The individual item-fit mean squares generated for the TAWF are presented in Table 4-1. The overall-fit mean square for item fit for the TAWF was .99. This fit statistic is evidence that the TAWF meets the goodness-of-fit criterion for the Rasch model, thereby supporting the reliability of the TAWF.

4-1 Table 4-1

Item Difficulties, Standardized Fit Mean Squares, and Standard Errors of Measurement for the Final Selection of Items on the TAWF, Based on the Rasch Latent Trait Item Analysis

Item	Item Difficulty	Standardized Fit Mean Square	Standard Error of Measurement
1-1	−2.30	0.07	0.23
1-2	−1.40	0.09	0.15
1-3	−0.99	0.00	0.12
1-4	−0.88	0.02	0.12
1-5	−0.84	0.07	0.12
1-6	−0.80	0.05	0.11
1-7	−0.65	0.17	0.11
1-8	−0.63	0.26	0.11
1-9	−0.58	0.02	0.10
1-10	−0.41	0.64	0.10
1-11	−0.33	−0.32	0.09
1-12	−0.29	0.47	0.09
1-13	−0.17	0.46	0.09
1-14	−0.15	−0.49	0.09
1-15	−0.05	−0.09	0.08
1-16	−0.05	0.16	0.08
1-17	−0.03	−0.22	0.08
1-18	0.01	−0.30	0.08
1-19	0.03	0.11	0.08
1-20	0.11	−0.40	0.08
1-21	0.22	−0.49	0.08
1-22	0.22	0.29	0.08
1-23	0.26	−0.47	0.08
1-24	0.36	−0.44	0.07
1-25	0.38	−0.62	0.07
1-26	0.38	−0.46	0.07
1-27	0.53	−1.01	0.07
1-28	0.67	−0.54	0.07
1-29	0.82	−0.89	0.06
1-30	0.85	0.77	0.06

4-1 Table 4-1
(Continued)
Item Difficulties, Standardized
Fit Mean Squares, and
Standard Errors of
Measurement for the Final
Selection of Items on the
TAWF, Based on the Rasch
Latent Trait Item Analysis

Item	Item Difficulty	Standardized Fit Mean Square	Standard Error of Measurement
1-31	0.98	1.32	0.06
1-32	1.37	1.25	0.06
1-33	1.39	−0.48	0.06
1-34	1.44	0.08	0.06
1-35	1.54	0.07	0.06
1-36	1.78	−0.43	0.05
1-37	1.90	1.14	0.05
2-1	−1.56	−0.06	0.16
2-2	−1.34	−0.07	0.14
2-3	−0.59	0.04	0.10
2-4	−0.40	0.04	0.10
2-5	−0.29	0.05	0.09
2-6	−0.23	0.38	0.09
2-7	−0.06	−0.16	0.08
2-8	0.01	0.55	0.08
2-9	0.04	−0.85	0.08
2-10	0.11	1.05	0.08
2-11	0.14	0.00	0.08
2-12	0.18	−0.60	0.08
2-13	0.19	−0.37	0.08
2-14	0.23	−0.43	0.08
2-15	0.26	−0.73	0.08
2-16	0.75	0.50	0.07
3-1	−1.26	0.09	0.14
3-2	−0.96	0.22	0.12
3-3	−0.52	−0.47	0.10
3-4	−0.42	−0.40	0.10
3-5	−0.23	−0.34	0.09
3-6	−0.11	0.34	0.09
3-7	0.08	1.46	0.08
3-8	0.08	0.14	0.08
3-9	0.76	0.47	0.07
3-10	0.88	−0.27	0.06
3-11	1.14	1.02	0.06
3-12	1.36	−1.46	0.06
4-1	−2.82	0.10	0.29
4-2	−2.21	0.04	0.22
4-3	−1.24	0.33	0.14
4-4	−0.96	0.05	0.12
4-5	−0.88	0.03	0.12
4-6	−0.87	0.03	0.12
4-7	−0.37	−0.01	0.10
4-8	−0.33	−0.02	0.09
4-9	−0.30	0.43	0.09
4-10	−0.10	0.00	0.09
4-11	0.13	0.76	0.08
4-12	0.22	0.18	0.08
4-13	0.55	0.53	0.07
4-14	0.78	1.88	0.06
4-15	1.13	−1.39	0.06

4-1 Table 4-1
(Continued)
Item Difficulties, Standardized
Fit Mean Squares, and
Standard Errors of
Measurement for the Final
Selection of Items on the
TAWF, Based on the Rasch
Latent Trait Item Analysis

Item	Item Difficulty	Standardized Fit Mean Square	Standard Error of Measurement
4-16	1.26	−0.03	0.06
4-17	1.29	1.72	0.06
4-18	1.43	1.94	0.06
4-19	1.47	1.91	0.06
4-20	1.62	1.99	0.05
4-21	1.84	0.33	0.05
5-1	−1.44	0.09	0.15
5-2	−1.30	−0.11	0.14
5-3	−1.28	0.02	0.14
5-4	−1.24	0.21	0.14
5-5	−1.18	0.05	0.13
5-6	−1.03	−0.04	0.13
5-7	−0.99	0.02	0.12
5-8	−0.88	−0.08	0.12
5-9	−0.73	−0.13	0.11
5-10	−0.51	−0.59	0.10
5-11	−0.38	0.04	0.10
5-12	−0.36	−0.28	0.09
5-13	0.09	−0.38	0.08
5-14	0.13	−1.20	0.08
5-15	0.15	−0.07	0.08
5-16	0.44	0.71	0.07
5-17	0.99	1.20	0.06
5-18	1.08	−1.08	0.06
5-19	1.09	0.00	0.06
5-20	1.39	−1.68	0.06
5-21	1.42	−0.27	0.06

TAWF BRIEF TEST

For the TAWF Brief Test, the overall-fit mean square for item fit was .99
($SD = .99$). The individual fit mean squares generated for each of the items on
the TAWF Brief Test are presented in Table 4-2. As with the complete TAWF,
these fit statistics are evidence that the TAWF Brief Test meets the goodness-
of-fit criterion for the Rasch model, thereby supporting its reliability.

ABILITY SCALE RELIABILITY

Indicated in Chapter 3 is an overall-fit mean square for person fit of .80 for the
complete TAWF. These statistics indicate that overall person reliability is
acceptable, though lower than might be expected. Because the majority of the
subjects in the sample were normally functioning (i.e., nondisordered) students
and adults, they found the naming tasks on the TAWF easy and thus produced
high scores. The resulting lack of variance in performance contributed to
producing a somewhat low person-fit correlation. For the TAWF Brief Test, the
overall-fit mean square for person fit is .65 ($SD = .91$).

4-2 **Table 4-2**

Item Difficulties, Standardized
Fit Mean Squares, and
Standard Errors of
Measurement for the Test
Items on the TAWF Brief Test,
Based on the Rasch Latent
Trait Item Analysis

Item	Item Difficulty	Standardized Fit Mean Square	Standard Error of Measurement
1-1	−2.30	0.07	0.23
1-4	−0.88	0.02	0.12
1-7	−0.65	0.17	0.11
1-10	−0.41	0.64	0.10
1-13	−0.17	0.46	0.09
1-15	−0.05	−0.09	0.08
1-19	0.03	0.11	0.08
1-21	0.22	−0.49	0.08
1-26	0.38	−0.46	0.07
1-28	0.67	−0.54	0.07
1-30	0.85	0.77	0.06
1-31	0.98	1.32	0.06
1-34	1.44	0.08	0.06
1-37	1.90	1.14	0.05
2-1	−1.56	−0.06	0.16
2-4	−0.40	0.04	0.10
2-7	−0.06	−0.16	0.08
2-10	0.11	1.05	0.08
2-13	0.19	−0.37	0.08
2-16	0.75	0.50	0.07
3-2	−0.96	0.22	0.12
3-5	−0.23	−0.34	0.09
3-8	0.08	0.14	0.08
3-11	1.14	1.02	0.06
4-2	−2.21	0.04	0.22
4-5	−0.88	0.03	0.12
4-8	−0.33	−0.02	0.09
4-10	−0.10	0.00	0.09
4-12	0.22	0.18	0.08
4-14	0.78	1.88	0.06
4-17	1.29	1.72	0.06
4-20	1.62	1.99	0.05
5-1	−1.44	0.09	0.15
5-3	−1.28	0.02	0.14
5-7	−0.99	0.02	0.12
5-10	−0.51	−0.59	0.10
5-13	0.09	−0.38	0.08
5-16	0.44	0.71	0.07
5-18	1.08	−1.08	0.06
5-19	1.09	0.00	0.06

STANDARD ERROR OF MEASUREMENT

Standard errors of measurement for the TAWF were generated from the Rasch
analysis. In addition, traditional reliability estimates are reported here for
comparison purposes.

The standard error of measurement estimates the amount of error
associated with an obtained score, thus indicating the level of confidence that
can be placed in the score (Salvia & Ysseldyke, 1988). The smaller the standard

errors of measurement, the more confident the examiner can be of the obtained scores. Table 4-3 presents the standard errors of measurement for the TAWF generated from the Rasch analysis of the entire sample. Unlike traditional estimates of reliability, which report group estimates of standard deviations of errors, the Rasch model yields an estimate of the error of measurement at each ability level (Hambleton, 1979). Thus, standard errors of measurement are reported in logit ability units (referred to here as TAWF-ability) for each obtained ability level (corresponding to each obtained raw score) on the TAWF. These standard errors of measurement were transformed to standard errors of measurement for each standard score using the following equation:

$$SEM_T = \frac{SD_T}{SD_A} SEM_A$$

where standard error of measurement for the transformed score (SEM_T) equals the standard deviation of the transformed score scale (SD_T) divided by the standard deviation of the Rasch ability scale (SD_A) times the standard error of measurement for each Rasch test score (SEM_A) (Hashway, 1978).

Transformations of Rasch standard errors of measurement for use with each TAWF standard score are presented in Table 4-4. As illustrated, standard

4-3 Table 4-3
Rasch Standard Errors of Measurement for TAWF-Ability Levels

Raw Scores	TAWF-Ability Level	Standard Error of Measurement	Raw Scores	TAWF-Ability Level	Standard Error of Measurement
60	.30	.22	85	1.61	.26
61	.34	.22	86	1.68	.26
62	.39	.22	87	1.74	.26
63	.44	.22	88	1.81	.27
64	.48	.22	89	1.89	.27
65	.53	.22	90	1.96	.28
66	.58	.22	91	2.04	.29
67	.63	.22	92	2.13	.29
68	.68	.22	93	2.21	.30
69	.72	.22	94	2.31	.31
70	.77	.22	95	2.41	.32
71	.82	.22	96	2.51	.33
72	.87	.23	97	2.62	.34
73	.93	.23	98	2.75	.36
74	.98	.23	99	2.88	.38
75	1.03	.23	100	3.03	.40
76	1.08	.23	101	3.21	.43
77	1.14	.23	102	3.41	.47
78	1.19	.24	103	3.65	.52
79	1.25	.24	104	3.95	.59
80	1.30	.24	105	4.37	.72
81	1.36	.24	106	5.08	1.01
82	1.42	.25	107	5.79	1.11
83	1.48	.25			
84	1.55	.25			

4-4 Table 4-4

Rasch Standard Errors of Measurement for TAWF Standard Scores on the Entire TAWF Sample

Standard Score	SEM	Standard Score	SEM
62	4.23	87	5.00
63	4.23	89	5.19
64	4.23	90	5.19
65	4.23	91	5.38
66	4.23	92	5.58
67	4.23	94	5.58
68	4.23	95	5.77
69	4.23	97	5.96
70	4.23	99	6.15
71	4.23	101	6.35
72	4.42	102	6.54
73	4.42	105	6.92
74	4.42	107	7.31
75	4.42	110	7.69
76	4.42	113	8.27
77	4.42	116	9.04
78	4.62	120	10.00
79	4.62	125	11.35
80	4.62	133	13.85
81	4.62	145	19.42
82	4.81	157	21.30
83	4.81	>157	>21.30
84	4.81		
85	5.00		
86	5.00		

errors of measurement generated from Rasch analyses vary depending on the region of the scale in which a score is obtained (Woodcock, 1973). That is, the TAWF standard errors for scores at the high end of the test are larger than those found in the middle range of the scale. This is particularly appropriate for language assessment utilizing the TAWF because the scores will be the most reliable for those subjects of greatest concern to the examiner—those whose word-finding scores fall within the middle ranges of the scale.

These standard errors of measurement generated from the Rasch analyses may be compared to traditional reliability estimates calculated using the Kuder-Richardson Formula 20 (KR-20). These traditional estimates are discussed in the next section, which also presents the standard errors of measurement computed for each grade and adult age group, using the KR-20 reliability coefficients.

TAWF BRIEF TEST

Standard errors of measurement for the TAWF Brief Test were generated from the Rasch analysis by the same methods described for the complete test. Table 4-5 presents the standard errors of measurement for the TAWF Brief Test generated from the Rasch analysis of the entire sample.

4-5 Table 4-5
Rasch Standard Errors of Measurement for TAWF-Ability Levels Obtained from the TAWF Brief Test

Raw Scores	TAWF-Ability Level	Standard Error of Measurement
10	−1.33	.40
11	−1.18	.39
12	−1.04	.38
13	−.90	.37
14	−.76	.37
15	−.63	.36
16	−.50	.36
17	−.37	.36
18	−.25	.35
19	−.12	.35
20	.00	.35
21	.12	.35
22	.25	.35
23	.37	.36
24	.50	.36
25	.63	.36
26	.76	.37
27	.90	.37
28	1.04	.38
29	1.18	.39
30	1.33	.40
31	1.50	.41
32	1.67	.42
33	1.86	.44
34	2.06	.47
35	2.30	.50
36	2.57	.55
37	2.91	.62
38	3.36	.74
39	4.10	1.02
40	4.82	1.30

Transformation of Rasch standard errors of measurement for use with each standard score on the TAWF Brief Test are presented in Table 4-6.

TRADITIONAL ESTIMATES OF RELIABILITY

ACCURACY SCORE

As noted, the goodness-of-fit statistic is the Rasch Latent Trait analog of traditional internal consistency reliability estimates. According to the fit statistics, the TAWF meets the goodness-of-fit criterion of the Rasch model, thereby supporting its reliability. One additional conventional reliability assessment was completed to examine the internal consistency of the TAWF items. The scores from the normal subjects in the standardization sample were analyzed using Kuder-Richardson Formula 20 (KR-20). Table 4-8 presents the

4-6 Table 4-6

Rasch Standard Errors of Measurement for TAWF Brief Test Standard Scores

Standard Score	SEM	Standard Score	SEM
44	6.26	74	6.10
46	6.10	76	6.26
48	6.10	79	6.43
50	5.93	81	6.59
52	5.93	83	6.76
54	5.93	86	6.92
56	5.77	89	7.25
58	5.77	92	7.75
60	5.77	96	8.24
62	5.77	100	9.07
64	5.77	105	10.22
66	5.93	112	12.20
68	5.93	124	16.81
70	5.93	135	21.46
72	6.10		

means, standard deviations, and KR-20 coefficients for the TAWF by grade- and age-level groupings. As described above, these coefficients were used in computing the traditional estimates of raw-score standard errors of measurement reported in Table 4-7. The KR-20 obtained for the pooled sample of subjects (all ages) was .85.

KR-20 coefficients were also computed for the subjects demonstrating word-finding problems ($N = 36$). The resulting coefficient, .85, provides further evidence of the TAWF's internal consistency and lends support to the TAWF as a reliable assessment tool for use with individuals with word-finding problems.

AGREEMENT BETWEEN TIME ASSESSMENTS USING TWO DIFFERENT PROCEDURES

The TAWF yields two procedures to assess response latencies. One procedure is the Actual Item Response Time measurement, which is a measurement of the

4-7 Table 4-7

Standard Errors of Measurement for Raw Scores by Grade/Age-Level Groupings for the TAWF

Grade/Age (in years-months)	N	Standard Error in Raw Score Points
Seventh	200	3.56
Eighth	200	3.53
Ninth	200	3.28
Tenth	200	3.24
Eleventh	200	2.41
Twelfth	200	2.94
20-0 to 39-11	201	2.54
40-0 to 59-11	200	2.80
60-0 to 80-0	152	3.36

Note: Standard errors of measurement are based on reliability coefficients generated from Kuder-Richardson Formula 20 internal consistency analyses, using the formula $SEM = SD \times \sqrt{1 - r}$.

4-8 Table 4-8

TAWF Internal Consistency: Kuder-Richardson Formula 20 Reliability Coefficients by Grade/Age-Level Groupings for Individuals in the Standardization Sample

Grade/Age (in years-months)	Mean Raw Score	SD	r
Seventh	88.6	8.9	.84
Eighth	90.3	8.2	.82
Ninth	93.0	8.2	.84
Tenth	93.5	7.2	.80
Eleventh	94.3	6.9	.80
Twelfth	96.2	6.7	.81
20-0 to 39-11	99.4	5.9	.82
40-0 to 59-11	97.4	7.0	.84
60-0 to 80-0	90.6	9.6	.88

interval between the presentation of the picture and the subject's response during the administration of Section 1 of the complete TAWF. The second analysis is the Estimated Item Response Time procedure, which is a judgment of whether the interval between the presentation of the picture and the subject's response to an item is greater than or less than 4 seconds. To determine whether the Estimated Item Response Time procedure should be used in the assessment of an individual's word-finding latencies, it was important to investigate how closely estimations of response delays agreed with results based on actual measurement of response delays. Of interest was whether an examiner's judgment about the speed of a subject's response (Estimated Item Response Time procedure) was consistent enough with the Actual Item Response Time measurement of that response to be reliable. Audio tapes and record forms of 45 normal learning subjects (5 in each grade- and age-level grouping) from the standardization sample were randomly selected for this comparison. An examiner trained in the administration of the TAWF listened to each of the audio tapes of Section 1, Picture Naming: Nouns, and applied the Estimated Item Response Time procedure. First, the examiner judged each response as either greater than or less than 4 seconds and tallied for each subject the number of responses in each of the two categories (category 1 = less than 4 seconds; category 2 = greater than 4 seconds). Second, the examiner measured the actual item response times by measuring to one-one hundredth of a second the item response time for each item. Then, based on that actual item response time, the examiner classified each response as greater than or less than 4 seconds. Frequency counts across subjects were then calculated for each of the two categories of latency scores—judged and timed. These counts were organized into a contingency table. The chi-square ($\chi^2 = 2.616$; $p > .05$) was not significant, indicating that classification of response delays using the Estimated Item Response Time procedure was not significantly different from classification based on the Actual Item Response Time measurement. For example, 8% of the judged response delays were classified as longer than 4 seconds and 7% of the actual item response times were longer than 4 seconds. That is, 92% of the judged response delays were classified as shorter than 4 seconds and 93% of the actual item response times were shorter than 4 seconds. Finally, the number of response delays of 4 seconds or longer obtained from the Estimated Item Response Time procedure was compared with the number of delays of 4 seconds or longer obtained from the Actual Item Response Time measurement, judged by timing with a stopwatch. The correlation between the two measurements of response delays of 4 seconds or longer was .97, reflecting nearly perfect agreement between the two methods. These findings suggest that a trained examiner employing the Estimated Item Response Time procedure on the TAWF can make judgments of response delays (4 seconds or longer) that are consistent with the Actual Item Response Time measurements of those items.

TEST-RETEST RELIABILITY

Two investigations were conducted to examine the stability of the TAWF over time, one involving adolescents and the other involving adults.

Test-Retest Study of Adolescents

The final edition of the TAWF (107 items) was administered in two different sessions to 15 seventh- and 15 eighth-grade normally learning students. The two sessions were 14 days apart. All students were considered average achievers by their classroom teachers; had not been referred for or received speech, special education, or psychological services; and had attained scores on the 1986 *Iowa Test of Basic Skills* between the fourth and eighth stanine. The study included monolingual students who were white (66%), black (20%), and Hispanic (14%). Of these, 47% were male and 53% were female. The students were from homes where at least one parent had high school education. Pearson product-moment correlations were computed on the accuracy raw scores and the Average Item Response Times obtained for the two sessions. The correlation between the accuracy raw scores was .93 (Test 1 mean accuracy raw score = 83.30, SD = 10.84; Test 2 mean accuracy raw score = 93.17, SD = 7.95). Although scores improved across the two testing situations, the magnitude of the correlation between the scores for the two testing sessions indicates high agreement between the two sets of results. Scores most likely improved because students were given the TAWF comprehension section following the first test administration and thus heard target words they were unable to name. The substantial test-retest reliability correlation (.93) from this investigation supports the stability reliability of the TAWF for assessing word-finding skills in adolescents (see Table 4-9).

4-9 Table 4-9
Test-Retest Reliability
Coefficients for Accuracy
Raw Scores and Average
Item Response Times for
Adolescent Students on the
Final Edition (107 Items) of
the TAWF

	r	N	Test 1		Test 2	
			M	SD	M	SD
Accuracy Raw Score for the TAWF	.93	30	83.30	10.80	93.20	7.90
Average Item Response Time	.81	30	2.44	.74	1.72	.62

Data from Swastek (1987).

Accuracy in naming is the main index for measuring TAWF performance. However, because the Average Item Response Time may be used to help interpret naming accuracy scores, its stability over time was also of interest. Thus, Pearson product-moment correlations were computed for the Average Item Response Times from Section 1 of the TAWF. This correlation coefficient of .81 was significant ($p < .001$), indicating good stability over time for the time index (Test 1 mean Average Item Response Time = 2.44, SD = .74; Test 2 mean Average Item Response Time = 1.72, SD = .61). Table 4-9 presents the test-retest correlations for the adolescents.

Test-Retest Study of Adults

A second test-retest investigation was conducted with 30 adults ranging in age from 23 to 53 years (mean age = 33 years) (D'Angelo, 1988). All adults were judged to be in the middle to upper-middle socioeconomic range, based on their level of educational attainment, and none had any remarkable medical history. The final edition of the TAWF was administered to the subjects twice, with an intervening period of 14 days. Pearson product-moment correlations were computed on the accuracy raw scores, yielding a coefficient of .85 (Test 1 mean accuracy score = 100.40, SD = 3.64; Test 2 mean accuracy score = 102.87, SD = 3.32). The magnitude of this correlation provides evidence for the test-retest reliability of the TAWF as a measurement of word-finding disorders for adults.

The stability of the Average Item Response Time was computed for Section 1 of the TAWF. The correlation coefficient for this time index on the two test occasions was .72 (Test 1 mean Average Item Response Time = 1.29, SD = .40; Test 2 mean Average Item Response Time = .95, SD = .24). Although significant ($p < .001$), this coefficient reflects less stability. Table 4-10 presents the test-retest correlations for the study of adults.

4-10 Table 4-10
Test-Retest Reliability
Coefficients for Accuracy
Scores and Average Item
Response Times for Adults
on the Final Edition (107
Items) of the TAWF

	r	N	Test 1		Test 2	
			M	SD	M	SD
Accuracy Score	.85	30	100.40	3.64	102.87	3.32
Average Item Response Time	.72	30	1.29	.40	.95	.24

Data from D'Angelo (1988).

CHAPTER FIVE

VALIDITY

According to Salvia and Ysseldyke (1988), "validity refers to the extent to which a test measures what its author or users claim it measures" (p. 101). Documentation of three types of validity is recommended: content validity, construct validity, and criterion-related validity (Anastasi, 1976; APA, *Joint Technical Standards for Educational and Psychological Testing,* 1984; Salvia & Ysseldyke, 1988).

CONTENT VALIDITY

Anastasi (1976) defined content validity as "the systematic examination of the test content to determine whether it covers a representative sample of the behavior domain to be measured" (pp. 134-135). More specifically, Salvia and Ysseldyke (1988) listed three factors that need to be considered to establish content validity: appropriateness of items, comprehensiveness of the item pool, and the assessment process utilized. These issues are discussed below.

The general and specific procedures employed in choosing the items and stimulus contexts for the TAWF were discussed earlier. In summary, item selection was guided by the results of time-honored investigations of word-finding skills reported in both the child and adult literature. Thus, variables purported to influence word finding such as target-word frequency, syntax, picturability, protypicality, and taxonomic level were considered. Stimulus context selection was also guided by findings reported in the literature that differences in word finding may be a function of the nature of the retrieval task.

One aspect of the item content validity of the TAWF yet to be discussed relates to the comprehensibility of its vocabulary items. By definition, an analysis of word finding must use vocabulary items that one is reasonably sure are within the receptive language of the intended population. Therefore, an analysis of word finding assumes that the subject knows the implied target word, thereby ensuring that the language assessment truly measures the ability to retrieve the intended word from the vocabulary. Otherwise, word knowledge, not word finding, would be assessed. This aspect of content validity was given major consideration when establishing the final pool of TAWF vocabulary items. As indicated, only items that the normative sample comprehended with 95% accuracy were included in the final version of the TAWF. The tables in Appendix A report the comprehension level achieved for each item by grade. A review of these tables suggests that the TAWF clearly has met the comprehension-level criterion necessary for valid assessment of adolescents' and adults' word-finding skills. The mean comprehension score for the standardization sample (indicating the mean percentage of comprehension of the TAWF items) was 99%. This supports the appropriateness of the TAWF vocabulary for assessing word-finding problems in students in seventh through twelfth grade and adults 20 through 80 years old.

With respect to the completeness of the item sample, the TAWF extends the traditional assessment of word finding, thereby providing the examiner with a broader format from which to analyze word-finding skills. For the most part, traditional analyses of word finding have been limited to picture naming of nouns. However, some studies of adults (Barton et al., 1969; Goodglass & Stuss, 1979) and more recent investigations of students have broadened these assessment models to include different stimulus contexts (Rudel, Denckla, & Broman, 1981; German, 1979) and various semantic categories (Denckla & Rudel, 1976b; German, 1985a). In addition, the syntactic and conceptual level of the target word has also been considered.

The format of the TAWF was based on these more recent investigations, thus providing the examiner with a more comprehensive assessment of word-finding skills. Items are presented in four stimulus contexts—an intersensory picture-naming task, two intrasensory auditory sentence tasks, and one intrasensory category-naming task. In addition, the syntactical and conceptual level of the target words has been considered. The TAWF assesses word-finding skills of target-word nouns, verbs, and category words. This broader assessment results in a more comprehensive and conclusive assessment of word-finding skills.

The third factor to evaluate when determining content validity is the procedures employed (Salvia & Ysseldyke, 1988). The TAWF employs two indices to evaluate word-finding skills—*accuracy* and *response time*. Results of previous investigations have varied with respect to these two indices. Some authors have reported group differences when using accuracy scores to assess word-finding skills of students (German, 1979; Wiig & Semel, 1976) and adults (Gardner, 1974a; Goodglass et al., 1966; Rockford & Williams, 1965). Other investigators have found response-time differences between control and experimental groups of students (Denckla et al., 1981; German, 1984, [1986] 1989; Wiig et al., 1982) and adults (Goodglass et al., 1984; Newcombe et al., 1965; Oldfield & Wingfield, 1965; Wingfield, 1968). However, both indices have been considered appropriate for assessing word-finding skills (German, 1984), hence both are employed. Specifically, the TAWF provides the examiner with scaled scores for the accuracy index, means and standard deviations for Average Item Response Times, and grade- and age-level standards for Estimated Item Response Times drawn from the normal subjects in the standardization sample. In addition, supplementary guidelines are provided for informal frequency counts for secondary word-finding characteristics such as extra verbalizations and gestures. These latter informal indices have been identified in the literature as clinically (Johnson & Myklebust, 1967; Wiig & Semel, 1984) and experimentally (German, 1984) differentiating students with word-finding problems from their peers with normal word-finding skills. Last, each target word missed is checked for comprehension, allowing the examiner to compare a particular individual's comprehension of the TAWF test items with the percentage comprehended by the normative sample in the same grade- or age-level group.

In summary, the appropriateness and comprehensiveness of the TAWF items have been established as being representative of the variables that have been identified in the literature as significantly influencing word-finding skills. The evaluation procedures employed are also representative of the indices determined to be appropriate for analyzing word-finding skills in adolescents and adults.

CRITERION-RELATED VALIDITY

According to Salvia and Ysseldyke (1988), "a test's criterion-related validity refers to the extent to which a person's score on a criterion measure can be estimated from the person's test score" (p. 137). The significance of this estimation is based on the correlation (validity coefficient) of two tests administered currently (concurrent validity) or on tests whose administration is separated by a specific time interval (predictive validity). The concurrent validity of the TAWF has been assessed.

Concurrent validity refers to the relationship between a test score and an established criterion measured at the same time. This criterion can be a formal or informal measure of what the test purports to assess (Anastasi, 1976). Although there is a standardized instrument designed to assess word-finding skills in elementary-age students *(Test of Word Finding,* German, [1986] 1989), there are no standardized language tests designed specifically to assess word-finding skills in adolescents. In addition, rapid automatic naming tasks and association naming tasks often used to assess children's naming skills appear not to be sensitive enough to draw out word-finding difficulties in adolescents. Therefore, the best comparison for concurrent validity for the TAWF appears to be two instruments used informally in the field to glean insights into word-finding skills in adolescents: the *Boston Naming Test* (Kaplan et al., 1976)—a picture-naming test of animals and objects for adults—and the *Upper Extension of the Expressive One-Word Picture Vocabulary Test* (Gardner, 1983)—a formal picture-naming task of objects and animals with internal consistency reliability coefficients ranging from .89 to .94.

A concurrent validity study on 15 seventh- and 15 eighth-grade normally learning students was conducted. All students were considered average achievers by their classroom teachers; had not been referred for or received speech, special education, or psychological services; and had attained scores on the 1986 *Iowa Test of Basic Skills* between stanines 4 and 8. The subjects included white (66%), black (20%), and Hispanic (14%) males (47%) and females (53%) and consisted of monolingual students from homes where at least one parent had high school education. Subjects were administered the TAWF (107 items), the *Boston Naming Test* (Kaplan et al., 1976), and the *Upper Extension of the Expressive One-Word Picture Vocabulary Test* (Gardner, 1983). Pearson product-moment correlations were computed between the TAWF accuracy score and accuracy score for each of these confrontation naming tests and are reported in Table 5-1. Moderate correlations were observed for the TAWF and the *Boston Naming Test* ($r = .66$) and for the TAWF and the *Upper Extension of the Expressive One-Word Picture Vocabulary Test* ($r = .62$). These values indicate that the TAWF correlates significantly with other confrontation naming tests typically used informally to assess word-finding skills in adolescents. The moderate nature of these two correlations, however, suggests that the TAWF does not yield a language assessment identical to these confrontation naming tests. The TAWF does provide the examiner with a broader assessment of word-finding skills in that observations of word-finding ability are made in intrasensory auditory tasks as well as the confrontation naming of pictures used by the two criterion measures.

Moreover, the correlation between the two criterion measures, the *Boston Naming Test* and the *Upper Extension of the Expressive One-Word Picture Vocabulary Test,* was .48 for this sample. Further evidence of the validity of the TAWF is supported by the finding that the correlation of the TAWF with each of the two criterion measures is higher than the correlation between those two measures. This may be explained in part by the comprehensiveness of the TAWF when compared with the other two measures. Both criterion measures require the subject to name pictured objects, a task similar to Section 1 of the TAWF. The TAWF, however, employs a series of additional tasks to assess naming, including sentence completion, naming to description, naming pictured verbs, and naming categories. These additional tasks contribute to a more comprehensive assessment of naming ability, resulting in correlations between the TAWF and the more restricted criterion measures that are higher than the correlation between the two.

In summary, the results of these investigations show that the TAWF correlates significantly with other measures presently used to assess students'

5-1 Table 5-1 Concurrent Validity Correlations Between the TAWF Accuracy Scores and Two Word-Finding Measures	Sample	*N*	Word-Finding Measures	Correlations with the TAWF
	Normally Learning Subjects	30	*Upper Extension of the Expressive One-Word Picture Vocabulary Test*	.62
			Boston Naming Test	.66

Data from Swastek (1987).

word-finding skills. Thus, these studies support the concurrent validity of the TAWF as a diagnostic instrument for assessing word-finding skills in adolescents.

CONSTRUCT VALIDITY

Construct validity refers to the extent to which a test measures the underlying traits or theoretical constructs it purports to measure. To determine construct validity, an author defines a construct, develops hypotheses with respect to that construct, and then tests those hypotheses to confirm the underlying constructs on which those hypotheses were based (Salvia & Ysseldyke, 1988). To the extent that one can verify these hypotheses, construct validity is established. The study of TAWF construct validity focused on hypotheses about word finding and developmental growth, dimensions (factors) measured, relationships between accuracy and time, and differentiation between subjects with word-finding disorders and subjects with normal word-finding ability. Evidence of the TAWF's construct validity is organized around the four hypotheses that follow.

1. The TAWF measures an aspect of expressive language related to development and maturation. Therefore, though the relationship need not be linear, it should be both predictable and consistent with changes in other cognitive abilities over time.

2. The TAWF contains five naming sections, each designed to assess an individual's word-finding skills. The TAWF was scaled as one global test rather than as five individual subtests. Therefore, when the five TAWF sections are factor analyzed, only one underlying factor should emerge, conceptualized as a word-finding factor.

3. Both response time and accuracy are indices used to define word-finding problems on the TAWF. Therefore, correlations between these two indices should be moderate to high.

4. The TAWF is a measure of word-finding skills. Therefore, indices used to define word finding on the TAWF should differentiate subjects with word-finding disorders from subjects with normal word-finding ability.

DEVELOPMENTAL DIFFERENCES

Comparisons of TAWF accuracy scores across grade- and age-level groupings in the standardization sample did indicate a relationship between maturation and performance on the TAWF. First, the comparison of accuracy scores in the student population reflected score differences across the groups studied. Table 5-2 presents the accuracy raw scores for each grade level. A 6 (grade) $\times$ 2

5-2 Table 5-2
TAWF Means and Standard Deviations for Accuracy Raw Scores of the Normal Subjects in the Standardization Sample, by Grade

Grade	N	Accuracy Score	
		Mean	SD
Seventh	200	88.6	8.9
Eighth	200	90.3	8.2
Ninth	200	93.0	8.2
Tenth	200	93.5	7.2
Eleventh	200	94.3	6.9
Twelfth	200	96.2	6.7

(sex) analysis of variance revealed a main effect for grade, $F(5,1188) = 25.48$, $p < .0001$, indicating significant differences in the accuracy scores between the grade levels. Duncan's Multiple-Range test, used to make comparisons between group means, indicated significantly lower mean accuracy scores for the seventh-grade students compared to those for each of the other grades. The mean accuracy scores of eighth-grade students were also significantly lower than those of students in the higher grades studied. The accuracy scores of ninth-, tenth-, and eleventh-grade students did not differ significantly from each other, but twelfth-grade students had significantly higher mean scores than those of the lower grades. This differentiation in TAWF accuracy scores of seventh-, eighth-, and twelfth-grade students from scores of students in all other grades supports the construct validity of the TAWF because it indicates a differentiation of scores with maturation across middle- and secondary-school grades.

Second, a comparison of accuracy scores in the adult population also indicated a consistent change in TAWF accuracy scores with advancing age. However, the observed relationship for adults is different from that observed for the adolescent sample. The comparison of accuracy scores at each of the adult age levels reflected reverse trends; that is, the accuracy scores of the adults in the standardization sample decreased with age. These scores are presented in Table 5-3. A 3 (age group) $\times$ 2 (sex) analysis of variance revealed a main effect for age, $F(2,547) = 48.89$, $p < .0001$, indicating significant differences in the accuracy scores of each of the three adult age groups (Duncan's Multiple-Range test). Interestingly, the adults in the 20-0 to 39-11 group showed improvement in word finding on the TAWF, and their accuracy scores were higher than those of the twelfth-grade students. However, both the 40-0 to 59-11 age group and

5-3 Table 5-3
TAWF Means and Standard Deviations for Accuracy Raw Scores of the Adults in the Standardization Sample, by Age Group

Age (in years-months)	N	Accuracy Score	
		Mean	SD
20-0 to 39-11	201	99.4	5.9
40-0 to 59-11	200	97.4	7.0
60-0 to 80-0	152	90.6	9.6

the 60 to 80 age group had lower accuracy scores than the younger adults, with the 60- to 80-year-olds manifesting the lowest scores in the adult sample. This pattern suggests that word-finding skills in the normal adult population may continue to improve up to middle age and then decline as an adult ages. In summary, the findings from these two analyses, which support group differentiation by the TAWF for all but the ninth through eleventh grades, reflect a relationship between TAWF test performance and maturation on the TAWF for both adolescents and adults.

TAWF Brief Test

Comparisons of TAWF accuracy scores for the Brief Test across age groupings in the standardization sample indicated the same relationship between maturation and performance observed on the complete TAWF. Table 5-4 presents the accuracy scores (raw scores) for each age-level grouping. For adolescents, accuracy in naming on the TAWF Brief Test improves with age, with score differences across age groups ranging from .03 to 2.30 points. In contrast, for adults the Brief Test shows only a slight decrease in word-finding skills from 20 to 60 years and a marked decrease in scores from 60 to 80 years. Older adults had the poorest performance on the TAWF Brief Test, with score differences across the age groups ranging from .74 to 3.59 points.

Comparison of time indices by grade and adult age groups reflected maturational differences similar to the comparisons of TAWF accuracy scores reported above. Tables 5-5 and 5-6 present Average Item Response Times for students at each grade level and for adults in the three age groups. With regard to the students, a 6 (grade) $\times$ 2 (sex) analysis of variance revealed a main effect for grade, $F(5,1102) = 5.98$, $p < .0001$, indicating significant differences in the Average Item Response Times between the grade levels. *Post hoc* tests

5-4 Table 5-4
Means and Standard Deviations for TAWF Brief Test Accuracy Raw Scores of Normal Subjects in the Standardization Sample, by Age

Age Groups (in years-months)	Accuracy Score	
	Mean	*SD*
12-0 to 12-11	33.23	3.74
13-0 to 13-11	33.53	3.38
14-0 to 14-11	34.00	3.51
15-0 to 15-11	34.94	3.13
16-0 to 16-11	35.17	2.87
17-0 to 17-11	35.50	2.89
18-0 to 19-11	35.53	2.53
20-0 to 39-11	37.30	2.33
40-0 to 59-11	36.56	2.67
60-0 to 80-0	33.71	3.87

5-5 Table 5-5

TAWF Means and Standard Deviations for Time Indices of Seventh- through Twelfth-Grade Normal Students in the Standardization Sample, by Grade

Grade	N	Average Item Response Time	
		Mean	SD
Seventh	179	1.72	.61
Eighth	180	1.63	.59
Ninth	177	1.55	.51
Tenth	178	1.57	.54
Eleventh	180	1.50	.49
Twelfth	156	1.47	.53

5-6 Table 5-6

TAWF Means and Standard Deviations for Time Indices of Normal Adults in the Standardization Sample, by Age Group

Age (in years-months)	N	Average Item Response Time	
		Mean	SD
20-0 to 39-11	161	1.39	.71
40-0 to 59-11	161	1.68	.57
60-0 to 80-0	127	2.11	.87

revealed that Average Item Response Time decreases from grade 7 to grade 9 and then appears to plateau from grade 9 to grade 12.

Comparison of the response times at each of the adult age levels reflected opposite trends, in that the Average Item Response Times of the adults in the standardization sample increased with age. A 3 (age group) $\times$ 2 (sex) analysis of variance revealed a main effect for age, $F(2,443) = 31.19$, $p < .0001$, indicating significant differences in the Average Item Response Times of the three adult age groups. Comparison of these means shows that mean item response time for the 20-0 to 39-11 group was shorter than that of the twelfth-grade students. However, the mean Average Item Response Times of both the 40-0 to 59-11 group and the 60-0 to 80-0 group increased with age and were significantly longer than the average time of younger adults. The 60- to 80-year-olds exhibited the longest Average Item Response Times in the entire sample. These findings suggest that response time in naming in the normal adult population may decrease through middle age and then increase thereafter.

In conclusion, the TAWF reflects the score differentiation across grade and age groups needed to support the construct validity of an instrument that assesses a skill shown to be highly correlated to chronological development in younger subjects. However, the relationship of retrieval skills and maturation in adolescents and adults, as defined by the TAWF, appears to be somewhat different from that observed in children. In children, word-retrieval skills (accuracy and speed of naming) have been shown to improve at least from first through fifth grade (German, [1986] 1989). However, in the adolescent and adult populations, this simple linear trend does not define the relationship between word finding and development. Instead, we observe a more complex relationship between retrieval and maturation. The pattern can best be described as (1) improvement in word-finding skills in middle-school and early secondary-school years; (2) a gradual leveling of word-finding skills in secondary school and early adulthood, with slight improvement in word-finding skills through middle age; and last (3) a decrease in word-finding skills after middle age, with older adults scoring more like early adolescents than their younger adult counterparts.

FACTOR ANALYSIS

Because the TAWF was intended as a test of word-finding skills across a series of different constrained naming tasks, it seemed important to determine whether the five sections that make up the TAWF were best explained by a single factor or by several factors. In order to identify the traits underlying the TAWF, a principal-components analysis was performed (with 1 in the diagonal), using the accuracy raw scores for each of the five sections of the TAWF, obtained for all subjects in the standardization sample ($N = 1753$). Using the criterion of an eigenvalue equal to or greater than one, only one principal component was extracted. This principal component had an eigenvalue of 2.81, accounting for 56% of the variance (see Table 5-7). The unrotated loadings of Sections 1, 2, 3, 4, and 5 on this first component (reported in Table 5-8) may be considered correlations of these scores with the component. The magnitude and similarity of these correlations reflect a high degree of overlap in the extent to which the

5-7 Table 5-7
Eigenvalues and Percentages of Total Variance Explained for the Principal Components in a Principal Components Analysis of TAWF Section Accuracy Scores for the Normal Subjects in the Standardization Sample ($N = 1753$)

Principal Component	1	2	3	4	5
Percentage of Total Variance	56.2%	11.9%	11.6%	10.2%	10.0%

5-8 Table 5-8
Loadings of TAWF Section Accuracy Scores on the First Principal Component in a Principal Components Analysis of the TAWF for the Normal Subjects in the Standardization Sample ($N = 1753$)

TAWF Section	Loading
1	.77
2	.77
3	.72
4	.73
5	.76

sections measure a common ability. This ability is conceptualized here as word-finding ability. These findings lend support to the construct validity of the TAWF as a test of word finding for adolescents and adults.

CORRELATIONS BETWEEN ACCURACY SCORES ON THE TAWF BRIEF TEST AND COMPLETE TEST

In order to determine the degree of relationship between naming accuracy on the TAWF Brief Test and naming accuracy on the entire TAWF instrument, TAWF raw scores and ability scores (Rasch) were correlated with TAWF Brief Test raw scores and ability scores (Rasch) for the adolescent and adult populations in the standardization sample. The correlation between the TAWF-ability scores obtained from the complete TAWF test and the TAWF-ability scores obtained from the TAWF Brief Test was $r = .86$ ($N = 1200$) for the adolescents, $r = .87$ ($N = 553$) for the adults, and $r = .87$ for combined groups ($N = 1753$). The correlation between the complete TAWF raw scores and the TAWF Brief Test raw scores was $r = .87$ ($N = 1200$) for the adolescents, $r = .92$ ($N = 553$) for the adults, and $r = .89$ for the combined groups ($N = 1753$). These correlations between the complete TAWF and the TAWF Brief Test are substantial and indicate a high degree of agreement between assessments of naming accuracy on the TAWF Brief Test and the complete TAWF. These findings support the use of the TAWF Brief Test in the assessment of word-finding skills in the adolescent and adult populations.

INTERCORRELATIONS BETWEEN WORD-FINDING INDICES

Two indices are used to define word-finding skills on the TAWF—accuracy and response time. In order to determine the relationship between these two word-finding measures, accuracy raw scores were correlated with the Average Item Response Time (Section 1). Table 5-9 presents these correlations for

5-9 Table 5-9
Intercorrelation Coefficients for Accuracy Raw Scores and Average Item Response Times of the Normal Subjects in the Standardization Sample, by Grade and Age

Grade/Age (in years-months)	N	Average Item Response Time and Accuracy Raw Score	Average Item Response Time and Accuracy Raw Score for Section 1
Seventh	200	−.47	−.45
Eighth	200	−.47	−.53
Ninth	200	−.51	−.57
Tenth	200	−.46	−.54
Eleventh	200	−.59	−.55
Twelfth	200	−.60	−.72
20-0 to 39-11	201	−.38	−.42
40-0 to 59-11	200	−.53	−.61
60-0 to 80-0	152	−.54	−.64

Note: $p > .001$ for all coefficients.

seventh through twelfth grades and for the three adult age groups. The correlation between Average Item Response Time and accuracy was $r = -.51$ for the total standardization sample; $r = -.52$ for the adolescent population alone; and $r = -.58$ for the adult population. The correlation between Average Item Response Time (Section 1) and the accuracy score on Section 1 was $r = -.56$ for the adolescents and $r = -.67$ for the adults. All of these correlations were significant at the .001 level. These moderate correlations indicate that accuracy scores of adolescents and adults decrease as their item response times increase. Although these correlations indicate a significant relationship between accuracy and the Average Item Response Time, they are not high enough to suggest that one measure is a perfect predictor of the other. Instead these indices measure different attributes of word finding that, when viewed together, provide a comprehensive assessment of word-finding skills.

INTERCORRELATIONS BETWEEN THE RESPONSE-TIME ASSESSMENTS

The TAWF yields two procedures to assess response latencies. One procedure is the Actual Item Response Time measurement, a measurement of the actual time interval between the presentation of the picture and the subject's response for items in Section 1 of the complete TAWF. The second is the Estimated Item Response Time procedure, a judgment of whether the time taken to respond to an item was greater than or less than 4 seconds. As discussed in Chapter 4, because both may be used in the assessment of a subject's word-finding latencies, it was of interest to assess the relationship between the actual and estimated measurement of response delays. An examiner used both the Estimated Item Response Time procedure and the Actual Item Response Time measurement with the TAWF results from 45 normally learning subjects. Pearson product-moment correlations between the two comparable scores obtained from these two procedures, judged and timed, were computed. The correlation was very high ($r = .97$, $p < .0001$; judged mean $= 3.16$, $SD = 3.52$; timed mean $= 2.60$, $SD = 3.31$). This correlation is so high that it appears these two response-time procedures are nearly interchangeable. That is, the Estimated Item Response Time procedure is an acceptable substitute for the Actual Item Response Time measurement in classifying response delays produced on the TAWF.

DISCRIMINATION BETWEEN GROUPS

The purpose of the TAWF is to assess the word-finding skills of students in grades 7 through 12 and adults 20 to 80 years of age. To be useful as a diagnostic instrument with good construct validity, the TAWF must show evidence of being able to differentiate subjects purported to have word-finding disorders from others assessed as having normal word-finding skills. Therefore, validity studies contrasting word-finding skills in individuals with and without word-finding disorders were considered necessary to establish the construct validity of the TAWF.

Validity studies of this nature were conducted on the TAWF, employing similar criteria to define the experimental and control groups in several different validity investigations. Although there is a standardized test developed to assess word-finding skills in elementary-school-age children, the *Test of Word Finding* (TWF) (German, [1986] 1989), and various diagnostic measures are available for use in informally assessing word-finding skills in students, presently there is no standardized diagnostic instrument designed for the sole purpose of assessing word-finding skills of adolescents. Therefore, the word-finding skills of the experimental groups were assessed informally using a three-fold process that included a speech pathologist/author interview, a review of the subject's IEP, and a word-finding questionnaire completed by a speech pathologist. Students in the experimental group (a) had been diagnosed as demonstrating word-finding problems by the speech and language pathologist in their school district; (b) had an Individualized Educational Plan indicating a diagnosis of word-finding difficulties along with remedial goals and objectives specific to word finding; and (c) showed evidence of at least 10 word-finding characteristics on a survey of word-finding behavior patterns completed by a speech and language pathologist (German, 1983). Last, the receptive language of the subjects in the experimental group was judged to be in the average range by their speech and language pathologist. This was documented by at least one of the following indicators: (a) average receptive language scores on the *Peabody Picture Vocabulary Test–Revised* (Dunn & Dunn, 1981); (b) no indication of receptive language problems on the Individualized Educational Plan, as defined by an absence of remediation goals or objectives specific to receptive language; and (c) positive responses on the questionnaire to the following word-finding characteristics, "knows the word he or she wants to retrieve, but can't think of it" and "has good understanding of oral language used in class."

In contrast, students assessed as having good word-finding skills were those whose word-finding questionnaire (completed by their teacher) reflected no evidence of word-finding difficulties. Subjects in the normally language-learning group were also placed full-time in regular classrooms and had not been referred for or received special education services, speech and language services, remedial reading services, or enrichment or gifted services. Control- and experimental-group subjects in each investigation were matched by sex, age, grade, ethnicity, and geographic region.

National Investigation

One validity investigation focused on students from across the country who exhibited word-finding problems. Thirty-six students diagnosed as having word-finding problems came from various sites included in the standardization. This experimental group (WF) was matched to a control group (NL) of 36 normally language-learning students. Experimental and control groups did not differ in age ($t = 1.54$; $p > .05$; WF $M = 187.58$ months, $SD = 18.21$; NL $M = 180.25$, $SD = 22.03$). Subjects ranged in age from 12 years 4 months to 18 years 6 months and were in seventh through twelfth grades. The criteria outlined previously for both the experimental and control groups were met. T tests for correlated samples were performed using the accuracy score, Total Item Response Times, and Average Item Response Times as the units of analysis. Group differences were shown to be significant for naming accuracy ($t = 5.736$; $p < .0001$; WF $M = 74.03$, $SD = 10.97$; NL $M = 87.97$, $SD = 9.62$), Total Item Response Times ($t = 5.29$; $p < .0001$; WF $M = 95.99$ seconds, $SD = 34.74$ seconds; NL $M = 60.68$ seconds, $SD = 19.94$ seconds), and Average Item Response Times ($t = -5.18$; $p < .001$; WF $M = 2.59$ seconds, $SD = .94$ seconds; NL $M = 1.66$ seconds, $SD = .53$ seconds). These findings indicate that the TAWF discriminates between groups of adolescent students with and without word-finding problems, thus providing support for the construct validity of the TAWF as an assessment tool for expressive language problems.

Chicago Metropolitan Area Investigation

Two investigations were conducted in the Chicago metropolitan area. The first investigation was an early validity study of the standardization edition of the TAWF. Twenty-four students with word-finding problems in Chicago metropolitan-area high schools were evaluated. The experimental group was matched to the control group (24 normally language-learning students) with respect to sex, race/ethnicity, geographic region, and socioeconomic level (defined by educational attainment level of parents). Subjects ranged in age from 12 years 4 months to 17 years 9 months and were in seventh through twelfth grades. Experimental and control groups did not differ in age ($t = .7006$; $p > .05$; WF $M = 176.33$ months, $SD = 21.11$; NL $M = 171.67$, $SD = 24.50$). The criteria outlined previously for both the experimental and control groups were met. T tests were performed using the accuracy score on the standardization edition of the TAWF (148 items) as the unit of analysis. Group differences were shown to be significant for the accuracy score ($t = 5.36$; $p < .0001$, WF $M = 100.29$, $SD = 13.37$; NL $M = 128.38$, $SD = 21.90$). These findings indicate that the TAWF discriminates between groups of adolescent students with and without word-finding problems, thus providing support for the construct validity of the TAWF as an assessment tool for expressive language problems in word finding.

Jesse (1988) conducted a third validity study, in which she evaluated 26 students with word-finding problems in high schools in La Grange, Winnetka, Palatine, Buffalo Grove, Oak Park, Carol Stream, and Riverside, Illinois. Experimental-group subjects were defined as having word-finding disorders using the same criteria as the earlier validity studies. These subjects were matched with 26 normal peers following the guidelines above. Subjects were given the final edition of the TAWF. Experimental and control groups did not differ in age ($t = .0416$; $p > .05$; WF $M = 188.58$ months, $SD = 16.19$; NL $M = 188.38$, $SD = 17.11$). Subjects ranged in age from 12 to 17 years and were in grade 7 and grades 9 through 12. T tests were performed using the accuracy score, Total Item Response Time, and the Average Item Response Time as the units of analysis. Group differences were shown to be significant for naming accuracy ($t = -6.6272$; $p < .0001$; WF $M = 83.31$, $SD = 9.80$; NL $M = 97.62$, $SD = 5.02$), Total Item Response Time ($t = 5.85$; $p < .0001$; WF $M = 87.35$ seconds, $SD = 28.19$ seconds; NL $M = 50.04$ seconds, $SD = 16.21$ seconds), and Average Item Response Time ($t = 5.95$; $p < .0001$; WF $M = 2.36$ seconds, $SD = .74$ seconds; NL $M = 1.35$ seconds, $SD = .44$ seconds), indicating that students with word-finding problems manifested significantly lower accuracy scores, longer Total Item Response Times, and longer Average Item Response Times than their normally language-learning peers on the TAWF. These three studies add further support to the validity of the TAWF as a measure for differentiating adolescents with and without word-finding problems.

Investigation with Adults

A fourth validity investigation was conducted with adult subjects. Landau (1988) administered the TAWF to 18 adult aphasic patients, either attending the University of Michigan Residential Aphasia Clinic (Communicative Disorders Clinic, University of Michigan, Ann Arbor) or receiving private speech/language therapy. Each subject's language was evaluated in a series of standardized tests and clinical observations. All subjects were given either the *Minnesota Test for Differential Diagnosis of Aphasia* (Schuell, 1972) or the *Boston Diagnostic Aphasia Examination* (Goodglass & Kaplan, 1972). Clinical types of aphasia were determined using a classification system associated with the Boston school of aphasia, cited in Taylor-Sarno (1981). Adults in the experimental group were judged by their attending speech and language pathologists as exhibiting language behaviors most like aphasic patients classified as having Broca's aphasia (6 subjects), conduction aphasia (6 subjects), Wernicke's aphasia (1 subject), and anomic aphasia (5 subjects).

Etiology of aphasia was either cerebrovascular (10 subjects), head trauma (5 subjects), or surgical intervention for physical or neurological abnormalities (3 subjects). Age of onset of aphasia ranged from 13 years to 81 years, with a mean of 43.8 years. The duration of aphasia ranged from 1 month to 6.5 years, with a mean duration of 2.5 years.

These subjects were matched for sex, age, race/ethnicity, geographic region, and educational level with normal adults drawn from the standardization sample. Subjects ranged in age from 19 years 4 months to 81 years 2 months, with a mean age of 49 years 6 months. Experimental and control groups did not differ significantly in age ($t = -05$; $p > .05$; adult aphasics $M = 590$ months,

$SD = 245.34$ months; normal adults $M = 594$, $SD = 233.47$). T tests were performed using the accuracy score, Total Item Response Time, and Average Item Response Time as the units of analysis. Group differences were shown to be significant for naming accuracy ($t = -5.65$; $p < .0001$; aphasic adults $M = 55.72$, $SD = 26.30$; normal adults $M = 93.06$, $SD = 9.7$), Total Item Response Time ($t = 4.32$; $p < .0001$; aphasic adults $M = 201.85$ seconds, $SD = 117.66$ seconds; normal adults $M = 74.41$ seconds, $SD = 42.87$ seconds), and Average Item Response Time ($t = -4.54$; $p < .0001$; aphasic adults $M = 5.90$ seconds, $SD = 3.44$ seconds; normal adults $M = 2.01$ seconds, $SD = 1.2$ seconds), indicating that adult aphasics manifested significantly lower accuracy scores, longer Total Item Response Times, and longer Average Item Response Times than their normal adult counterparts on the TAWF. These findings support the construct validity of the TAWF as a diagnostic instrument for the identification of word-finding disorders in adults with aphasia.

TAWF Brief Test

The purpose of the TAWF Brief Test is to provide a word-finding assessment procedure for adolescents or adults who, for specific clinical reasons, cannot be given the complete TAWF. Therefore, to be a useful instrument with good construct validity, the TAWF Brief Test must differentiate individuals purported to have word-finding disorders from others assessed as having normal word-finding skills. An analysis contrasting word-finding skills in adults with and without word-finding disorders was performed on data from the adult validity sample (Landau, 1988). In this analysis, however, record forms from the 36 adult participants were rescored considering only those items on the TAWF Brief Test. T tests were performed using the accuracy score from the Brief Test as the unit of analysis. Group differences were shown to be significant for naming accuracy ($t = -5.36$; $p < .0001$; aphasic adults $M = 21.33$, $SD = 10.01$; normal adults $M = 34.61$, $SD = 3.07$). These findings support the construct validity of the TAWF Brief Test as a diagnostic procedure for the assessment of word-finding disorders in adults with aphasia.

ANALYSES OF WORD-FINDING PROFILES

In addition to the analyses indicating that the TAWF discriminates between individuals with and without word-finding problems, an analysis was conducted to determine if naming profiles can be identified on the TAWF. Jesse (1988) studied the speed and accuracy of the students in her validity study. The subjects were 26 students with word-finding problems and 26 normally language-learning students. The experimental and control groups were matched with respect to sex, race/ethnicity, geographic region, and socioeconomic level. Experimental and control groups did not differ in age ($t = .0416$, $p > .05$; WF $M = 188.58$ months, SD 16.19; NL $M = 188.38$, $SD = 17.11$). Subjects ranged in age from 12 to 17 years and were in grade 7 and grades 9 through 12. Three types of naming profiles were explored: accuracy, time, and accuracy and time. Adolescents' accuracy raw scores and Average Item Response Times on the TAWF constituted the units of analysis.

First, in order to establish profiles that represent naming accuracy, subjects were subdivided based on the magnitude of the difference between their scores and the mean accuracy score of the matched group of normal students. Three profiles emerged: Inaccurate Namers, Accurate Namers, and Very Accurate Namers. *Inaccurate Namers* were students whose accuracy scores were one standard deviation below the mean for normally language-learning students (below 92.6). *Accurate Namers* had accuracy scores within $-1\ SD$ and $+1\ SD$ of the mean for the normally language-learning subjects (between 92.60 and 102.0). *Very Accurate Namers* had accuracy scores equal to or greater than 1 SD above the mean for the normally language-learning subjects (above 102.0). A chi-square test was significant beyond the .001 level ($\chi^2 = 19.19$, $p < .001$), indicating a significant difference between the distribution of students with word-finding problems and their normally language-learning counterparts in the three subcategories. That is, 69% of the students with word-finding problems were classified in the Inaccurate naming category while only 12% of the normal subjects were so classified. For Accurate Namers and Very Accurate Namers, 73% and 15% of the normal language group were classified, respectively, in contrast to 31% of the subjects with word-finding problems classified as Accurate Namers and no word-finding students classified as Very Accurate Namers. These findings support the use of the accuracy index to indentify students with word-finding problems.

In order to establish profiles that represent the time students take to name target words on the TAWF, subjects were again subdivided based on the magnitude of the difference between their time and the mean of the Average Item Response Times of the matched group of normal students. Three naming profiles emerged: Slow Namers, Fast Namers, and Very Fast Namers. *Slow Namers* referred to students whose speed of naming was 1 SD above the mean for the normally language-learning subjects (above 1.79 seconds). *Average Namers* had times that fell within $-1\ SD$ and $+1\ SD$ of the mean for the normally language-learning students (between .91 seconds and 1.79 seconds). *Fast Namers* had times below .91 seconds. A chi-square test was significant beyond the .001 level ($\chi^2 = 20.92$, $p < .0001$), indicating a significant difference between the distribution of students with word-finding problems and the normally language-learning sample in the three groups classified by naming speed. The majority (77%) of the students with word-finding problems were classified as Slow Namers, in contrast to only 15% of the normally language-learning students. Only 23% of the experimental subjects were considered Average Namers, while 65% of the control group were so classified. Nineteen percent of the normally language-learning students were classified as Fast

Namers, whereas no subjects in the experimental group were so classified. As with accuracy scores, these findings support the appropriateness of using the time index to identify adolescents with word-finding problems.

Last, in order to establish profiles that represent both speed and accuracy in naming on the TAWF, subjects were again subdivided with respect to the differences between their time and accuracy scores and the corresponding means for the matched group of normally language-learning students. In order to establish four naming profiles, the Very Accurate and Accurate Namer categories were combined and the Average and Fast Namer categories were combined. The following four naming categories were considered: Slow and Inaccurate Namers, Fast and Inaccurate Namers, Slow and Accurate Namers, and Fast and Accurate Namers. *Slow and Inaccurate Namers* were students whose times were 1 *SD* above the normally language-learning mean (above 1.79 seconds) and whose accuracy scores fell 1 *SD* below the normally language-learning mean (below 92.6). *Fast and Inaccurate Namers* had times that were within or below 1 *SD* of the normally language-learning mean (below 1.79 seconds) and had accuracy scores at least 1 *SD* below the normally language-learning mean (below 92.6). *Slow and Accurate Namers* had times at least 1 *SD* above the normally language-learning mean (above 1.79 seconds) and had accuracy scores within or above −1 *SD* of the normally language-learning mean (above 92.6). Finally, *Fast and Accurate Namers* had times within or below 1 *SD* of the normally language-learning mean (below 1.79 seconds) and accuracy scores within or above −1 *SD* of the normally language-learning mean (above 92.6). This last group represented students who did not manifest word-finding problems on the TAWF.

A chi-square test was significant beyond the .001 level ($\chi^2 = 24.04$, $p < .0001$), indicating a significant difference between the distribution of students with word-finding problems and the normally language-learning adolescents in the four naming profiles. An analysis of the distributions showed that the majority of students with word-finding problems fell in the Slow and Inaccurate category (62%), while only 4% of the normally language-learning subjects fell in this category. Seventy-seven percent of the latter group were placed in the Fast and Accurate category (no word-finding problems), but only 15% of the experimental group were so classified. Fifteen percent of the students with word-finding problems fell in the Slow and Accurate category and 8% in the Fast and Inaccurate category. In contrast, 11% of the normal sample were placed in the Slow and Accurate and 8% in the Fast and Inaccurate category. Although students in the experimental group did exhibit profiles of Slow and Accurate Namers and Fast and Inaccurate Namers, these were similarly represented in the control group. It appears that the majority of adolescents with word-finding disorders in this investigation exhibited a profile of a Slow and Inaccurate Namer, indicating difficulties with both naming accuracy and speed.

In summary, the results of this investigation show that the TAWF discriminates between students known to have word-finding problems and students with normal language skills. Together, the series of investigations discussed here strongly supports the use of the TAWF as a diagnostic instrument to assess word-finding skills and provides additional support for the construct validity of the TAWF as an assessment tool for word-finding skills in adolescent students.

ESTABLISHING WORD-FINDING PROFILES USING THE ESTIMATED ITEM RESPONSE TIME PROCEDURE

Two investigations were conducted to establish the validity of the Estimated Item Response Time procedure in establishing profiles of word finding. The first investigation was conducted to determine if the Estimated Item Response Time procedure would differentiate experimental and control groups with respect to their word-finding profiles. The performance of the 36 students diagnosed as having word-finding problems at the various sites included in the standardization program was compared to that of their matched control group (36 normally language-learning students). Experimental and control groups did not differ in age ($t = 1.54$, $p > .05$; WF $M = 187.58$ months, $SD = 8.21$; NL $M = 180.25$, $SD = 22.03$). Subjects ranged in age from 12 years 4 months to 18 years 6 months and were in grades 7 through 12. The criteria outlined previously for both the experimental and control groups were met. In this investigation, two response categories were considered. Subjects were judged to be Slow Namers or Fast Namers based on a frequency count of the number of their responses that were either slower or faster than 4 seconds. Grade-Level Standards, indicating the number of response delays (4 seconds or longer) for each grade level, were used to classify students as Slow Namers or Fast Namers. Students who exhibited more response delays (4 seconds or longer) than the Grade-Level Standard were classified as Slow Namers. Students who exhibited the same or fewer response delays (4 seconds or longer) than the Grade-Level Standard were classified as Fast Namers. A chi-square test was significant beyond the .001 level ($\chi^2 = 17.75$; $p > .0001$), indicating a significant difference in the distribution of the experimental and control groups in the two naming-speed categories. The majority (65%) of the students with word-finding problems were classified as Slow Namers, in contrast to only 15% of the normally language-learning students so classified. Only 35% of the experimental subjects were considered Fast Namers, while 85% of the control group were so classified. These findings indicate that the Estimated Item Response Time procedure differentiates between students with and without word-finding disorders. In addition, by indicating that a greater percentage of the students with word-finding problems were classified as Slow Namers, these findings support the appropriateness of using the Estimated Item Response Time procedure to identify those adolescents with word-finding problems who also have slow response times.

In a second investigation, the Estimated Item Response Time procedure was compared to the Actual Item Response Time measurement to determine if the two assessments would result in similar distributions of subjects in the Slow Namer and Fast Namer categories. The time scores of the same 36 students with word-finding problems described above were studied. In this investigation, two response categories were considered, Slow Namers and Fast Namers. Subjects were first classified by the Actual Item Response Time measurement. Slow Namers were subjects whose Average Item Response Time was above the Grade-Level Standard. Fast Namers were subjects whose Average Item Response Time was equal to or less than the Grade Level Standard based on their grade. Second, subjects were classified as Slow Namers or Fast Namers based on whether they exhibited more or fewer response delays (4 seconds or longer) than the Grade-Level Standards for this time score. Students with scores above their respective Grade-Level Standard were classified as Slow Namers. Students with scores equal to or lower than their respective Grade-Level Standard were classified as Fast Namers. A chi-square test of the distributions of Slow Namers and Fast Namers, constructed by using the Average Item Response Time and the Estimated Item Response Time, was not significant at the .05 level ($\chi^2 = .0657$, $p > .05$). Sixty-five percent of the students with word-finding problems were classified as Slow Namers using the Estimated Item Response Time procedure, in comparison to 68% of the subjects so classified using the Actual Item Response Time measurement. Similarly, 35% of the subjects were considered Fast Namers using the Estimated Item Response Time procedure, and 32% were so classified employing the Actual Item Response Time measurement. These findings indicate that use of the Estimated Item Response Time procedure results in so similar a classification of Slow Namers or Fast Namers as one resulting from the Actual Item Response Time measurement that examiners can use the Estimated Item Response Time procedure with confidence in determining response-time profiles for students with word-finding disorders.

REFERENCES

Ahrens, R. (1977). Disturbances of word finding of compound nouns in aphasics. *Archives of Psychiatry, 224,* 73–87.

American Psychological Association. (1984). *Joint technical standards for educational and psychological testing.* Washington, DC: Author.

Anastasi, A. (1976). *Psychological testing.* New York: Macmillan.

Baker H. J., & Leland, B. (1967). *Detroit Tests of Learning Aptitude.* Indianapolis: Bobbs-Merrill.

Barten, S.S. (1979). Development of gestures. In N. R. Smith & M. B. Franklin (Eds.), *Symbolic functioning in childhood* (pp. 139–151). Hillsdale, NJ: Lawrence Erlbaum.

Barton, M., Maruszewski, D., & Urrea, D. (1969). Variations of stimulus context and its effect on word finding ability in aphasics. *Cortex, 5,* 351–364.

Battig, W. F., & Montague, W. E. (1969). Category norms of verbal items in 56 categories: A replication and extension of the Connecticut category norms. *Journal of Experimental Psychology Monographs, 80*(3, Pt. 2).

Benson, D. F. (1983). Naming disorders. In M. Studdert-Kennedy (Ed.), *Psychobiology of language* (pp. 126–128). Cambridge: MIT Press.

Berman, M., & Peelle, L. M. (1967). Self-generated cues: A method for aiding aphasic and apractic patients. *Journal of Speech and Hearing Disorders, 32,* 372–376.

Blumenthal, S. H. (1980). A study of the relationship between speed of retrieval of verbal information and patterns of oral reading errors. *Journal of Learning Disabilities, 13,* 568–570.

Boysen, A., & Cullinan, W. (1971). Object-naming latency in stuttering and nonstuttering children. *Journal of Speech and Hearing Research, 14,* 728–738.

Canter, G. (1972, November). *The nature of word-retrieval disturbances in aphasia.* Paper presented at the annual meeting of the American Speech and Hearing Association, San Francisco.

Carroll, H. B., Davies, P., & Richman, B. (1971). *American Heritage word frequency book.* Boston: Houghton-Mifflin.

Cohn, R. (1970). Amnestic aphasia and other disturbances in naming. *Archives of Neurology, 22,* 515–520.

Coughlan, A. K., & Warrington, E. K. (1978). Word-comprehension and word retrieval in patients with localized cerebral lesions. *Brain, 101,* 163–185.

D'Angelo, T. (1988). [Test-retest reliability of the *Test of Adolescent/Adult Word Finding (TAWF)*]. Unpublished raw data.

Denckla, M. B., & Rudel, R. (1974). Rapid "automatized" naming of pictured objects, colors, letters and numbers by normal children. *Cortex, 10,* 186–202.

Denckla, M. B., & Rudel, R. (1976a). Naming of object drawings by dyslexic and other learning disabled children. *Brain and Language, 3,* 1–16.

Denckla, M. B., & Rudel, R. (1976b). Rapid "automatized" naming (R.A.N.): Dyslexia differentiated from other learning disabilities. *Neuropsychologia, 14,* 471–479.

Denckla, M. B., Rudel, R. G., & Broman, M. (1981). Tests that discriminate between dyslexic and other learning-disabled boys. *Brain and Language, 13,* 118–129.

Dunn, L. M., & Dunn, L. M. (1981). *Peabody Picture Vocabulary Test–Revised.* Circle Pines, MN: American Guidance Service.

Eakin, S., & Douglas, V. I. (1971). "Automatization" and oral reading problems in children. *Journal of Learning Disabilities, 4,* 31–38.

Evens, M., Litowitz, B., Markowitz, J., Smith, R., & Werner, O. (1983). *Lexical-semantic relationships: A comparative survey.* Edmonton, Alberta, Canada: Linguistic Research.

Felton, R. H. (1983). *Dysnomia and its relationship to subtypes of reading disabilities.* Unpublished doctoral dissertation, The University of North Carolina at Greensboro.

Fried-Oken, M. B. (1984). *The development of naming skills in normal and language deficient children.* Unpublished doctoral dissertation, Boston University.

Gardner, H. (1974a). The naming of objects and symbols by children and aphasic patients. *Journal of Psycholinguistic Research, 3*(2), 133–149.

Gardner, H. (1974b). The naming and recognition of written symbols in aphasic and alexic patients. *Journal of Communication Disorders, 7,* 141–153.

Gardner, M. F. (1983). *Upper Extension of the Expressive One-Word Picture Vocabulary Test.* Novato, CA: Academic Therapy.

Garnett, K., & Fleischner, J. E. (1983). Automatization and basic fact performance of normal and learning disabled children. *Learning Disability Quarterly, 6,* 223–231.

German, D. J. N. (1979). Word-finding skills in children with learning disabilities. *Journal of Learning Disabilities, 12,* 176–181.

German, D. J. N. (1982). Word-finding substitutions in children with learning disabilities. *Language, Speech, and Hearing Services in the Schools, 13,* 223–230.

German, D. J. (1983). I know it but I can't think of it: Word retrieval difficulties. *Academic Therapy, 18,* 539–545.

German, D. J. (1984). Diagnosis of word-finding disorders in children with learning disabilities. *Journal of Learning Disabilities, 17,* 353–358.

German, D. J. (1985a). The use of specific semantic word categories in the diagnosis of dysnomic learning disabled children. *British Journal of Disorders of Communication, 20,* 143–154.

German, D. J. (1985b). *Children's word-finding profiles in constrained naming tasks.* Paper presented at the annual meeting of American Speech-Language-Hearing Association, Washington, DC.

German, D. J. ([1986] 1989). *National College of Education Test of Word Finding.* Allen, TX: DLM Teaching Resources.

German, D. J. (1987a). Spontaneous language profiles of children with word-finding problems. *Language, Speech, and Hearing Services in the Schools, 18,* 217–230.

German, D. J. (1987b, November). *Word finding skills in constrained and spontaneous naming tasks.* Paper presented at the annual meeting of the American Speech-Language-Hearing Association, New Orleans.

German, D. J. (in press). *Test of Word Finding in Discourse (TWF-D)*. Allen, TX: DLM.

German, D. J., & Fried-Oken, M. (1984, November). *The assessment of word-finding problems in children*. Miniseminar presented at the annual meeting of the American Speech-Language-Hearing Association, San Francisco.

Geschwind, N. (1967). The varieties of naming errors. *Cortex, 3,* 97–112.

Goldstein, K. (1948). *Language and language disturbances.* New York: Grune & Stratton.

Goodglass, H. (1981). The syndromes of aphasia: Similarities and differences in neurolinguistic features. *Topics in Language Disorders, 1*(4), 1–14.

Goodglass, H., & Kaplan, E. (1972). *Boston Diagnostic Aphasia Examination.* Philadelphia: Lea & Febiger.

Goodglass, H., Klein, B., Carey, P., & Jones, K. (1966). Specific semantic word categories in aphasia. *Cortex, 2,* 74–89.

Goodglass, H., & Stuss, D. T. (1979). Naming to picture versus description in three aphasic subgroups. *Cortex, 15,* 199–211.

Goodglass, H., Theurkauf, J., & Wingfield, A. (1984). Naming latencies as evidence for two modes of lexical retrieval. *Applied Psycholinguistics, 5,* 135–146.

Halsey, W. D. (Editorial Director), & Morris, C. G. (Ed.). (1977). *Macmillan dictionary for children.* New York: Macmillan.

Hambleton, R. (1979). Latent trait models and their applications. In R. Traub (Ed.), *New directions for testing and measurement: Methodological developments* (pp. 13–32). San Francisco: Jossey-Bass.

Harris, A. J., & Jacobson, M. D. (1972). *Basic elementary reading vocabularies.* London, England: Collier Macmillan Limited.

Hashway, R. M. (1978). *Objective mental measurement: Individual and program evaluation using the Rasch model.* New York: Praeger.

Hatfield, F. M. (1981). Analysis and remediation of aphasia in the USSR: The contribution of A. R. Luria. *Journal of Speech and Hearing Disorders, 46,* 338–347.

Head, H. (1926). *Aphasia and kindred disorders of speech.* Cambridge, England: Cambridge University Press.

Jansky, J., & DeHirsch, K. (1973). *Preventing reading failure.* New York: Harper & Row.

Jesse, P. (1988). *Validity study of the National College of Education Test Of Adolescent Word Finding (TAWF).* Unpublished master's thesis, National College of Education, Evanston, IL.

Johnson, D., & Myklebust, H. (1967). *Learning disabilities: Educational principles and practices.* New York: Grune & Stratton.

Johnson, K., Markert, L., Shuy, R. W., Squire, J. R., & Venezky, R. L. (1979). *Ginn basal readers, Grades K-6.* Lexington, MA: Ginn.

Kail, R., & Leonard, L. (1986). Word-finding abilities in language-impaired children. *ASHA Monographs, 25.*

Kaplan, E., Goodglass, H., & Weintraub, S. (1976). *Boston Naming Test (experimental ed.).* Boston: Veterans Administration Hospital.

Katz, R., & Shankweiler, D. (1985). Repetitive naming and the detection of word retrieval deficits in the beginning reader. *Cortex, 21,* 617–625.

Kaufman, A. S., & Doppelt, J. E. (1976). Analysis of WISC-R standardization data in terms of the stratification variables. *Child Development, 47,* 165–171.

Kaufman, A. S., & Kaufman, N. L. (1975). Social-class differences on the McCarthy Scales of Children's Abilities. *Perceptual and Motor Skills, 41,* 205–206.

Kaufman, A., & Kaufman, N. (1983). *Kaufman Assessment Battery for Children, interpretive manual.* Circle Pines, MN: American Guidance Service.

Kohn, S., & Goodglass, H. (1985). Picture-naming in aphasia. *Brain and Language, 24,* 266–283.

Landau, C. C. (1988). [Adult construct validity investigation of the *Test of Adolescent/Adult Word Finding*]. Unpublished raw data.

Le Jeune, J. P. (1974). The vocabulary of aphasic speakers (Doctoral dissertation, University of Victoria, Canada, 1974). *Dissertation Abstracts International, 35,* 4146-08B.

Leonard, L. B., Nippold, M. A., Kail, R., & Hale, C. A. (1983). Picture naming in language-impaired children: Differentiating lexical storage from retrieval. *Journal of Speech and Hearing Research, 26,* 609–615.

Lewis, R. B., & Kass, C. E. (1982). Labeling and recall in learning disabled students. *Journal of Learning Disabilities, 15,* 238–241.

Love, R. J., & Webb, W. G. (1977). The efficacy of cueing techniques in Broca's aphasia. *Journal of Speech & Hearing Disorders, 42,* 170–178.

Luria, A. R. (1966). *Higher cortical functions in man.* New York: Basic Books.

Luria, A. R. (1980). *Higher cortical functions in man* (rev. ed.). New York: Basic Books.

Lyons, J. (1977). *Semantics* (vol. 1). Cambridge, England: Cambridge University Press.

Marshall, J., & Newcomb, F. (1971). Syntactic class as a determinant of word-retrieval in normal and dyslexic subjects. *Nature, 243,* 418.

Marshall, R. C. (1976). Word retrieval of aphasic adults. *Journal of Speech and Hearing Disorders, 41,* 444–451.

Mattis, S., French, J., & Rapin, I. (1975). Dyslexia in children and young adults: Three independent neurological syndromes. *Developmental Medicine and Child Neurology, 17,* 150–163.

McCarthy, D. (1970). *McCarthy Scales of Children's Abilities.* New York: Psychological Corporation.

Morris, W. (Ed.). (1974). *The Ginn intermediate dictionary.* Middletown, CT: Ginn.

Nielsen, J. M. (1962). *Agnosia, apraxia, aphasia: Their value in cerebral localization.* New York: Hafner.

Newcombe, F., Oldfield, P., & Wingfield, A. (1965). Object naming by dysphasic patients. *Nature, 207,* 1217–1220.

Oldfield, R. C. (1966). Things, words, and the brain. *Quarterly Journal of Experimental Psychology, 18,* 341–353.

Oldfield, R. C., & Wingfield, A. (1965). Response latencies in naming objects. *Quarterly Journal of Experimental Psychology, 17,* 273–281.

Pease, D. M., & Goodglass, H. (1978). The effects of cuing on picture naming in aphasia. *Cortex, 14,* 178–189.

Perfetti, C. A., Finger, E., & Hogaboam, T. (1978). Sources of vocalization latency differences between skilled and less skilled young readers. *Journal of Educational Psychology, 70,* 730–739.

Riegel, K. F. (1970). The language acquisition process: A reinterpretation of selected research findings. In L. R. Goulet & P. B. Baltes (Eds.), *Life-span developmental psychology* (pp. 357–399). New York: Academic Press.

Rinnert, C., & Whitaker, H. A. (1973). Semantic confusions by aphasic patients. *Cortex, 9,* 56–81.

Rochford, G. (1971). A study of naming errors in dysphasic and in demented patients. *Neuropsychologia, 9,* 437–443.

Rochford, G., & Williams, M. (1962). Studies in the development and breakdown of the use of names: Part 1. The relationship between nominal dysphasia and the acquisition of vocabulary in childhood. *Journal of Neurology, Neurosurgery, and Psychiatry, 25,* 222–227.

Rochford, G., & Williams, M. (1965). Studies in the development and breakdown of the use of names: Part 4. The effects of word frequency. *Journal of Neurology, Neurosurgery, and Psychiatry, 28,* 407–413.

Rosch, E. (1975). Cognitive representations of semantic categories. *Journal of Experimental Psychology, 104*(3), 192–233.

Rosch E. (1977). Classification of real-world objects: Origins and representations in cognition. In P. N. Johnson-Laird & P. C. Wason (Eds.), *Thinking: Reading in cognitive science* (pp. 212–222). Cambridge, England: Cambridge University Press.

Rosch, E., Mervis, C., Gray, W., Johnson, D., & Boyes-Braem, P. (1976). Basic objects in natural categories. *Cognitive Psychology, 8,* 382–439.

Rubin, H., & Liberman, I. (1983). Exploring the oral and written language errors made by language disabled children. *Annals of Dyslexia, 33,* 111–120.

Rudel, R. G., Denckla, M. B., & Broman, M. (1981). The effect of varying stimulus context on word-finding ability: Dyslexia further differentiated from other learning disabilities. *Brain and Language, 13,* 130–144.

Rudel, R. G., Denckla, M. B., Broman, M., & Hirsch, S. (1980). Word-finding as a function of stimulus context: Children compared with aphasic adults. *Brain and Language, 10,* 111–119.

Rutherford, D., & Telser, E. (1967). *Word-finding abilities of kindergarten and first-grade children.* Paper presented at the annual meeting of the American Speech and Hearing Association, Chicago.

Salvia, J., & Ysseldyke, J. E. (1988). *Assessment in special and remedial education* (5th ed.). Boston: Houghton-Mifflin.

Schuell, H. (1972). *Minnesota Test for Differential Diagnosis of Aphasia.* Minneapolis: University of Minnesota Press.

Schuell, H., & Jenkins, J. (1959). The nature of language deficit in aphasia. *Psychological Review, 66*(1), 45–67.

Semel, E. M., & Wiig, E. H. (1980). *Clinical Evaluation of Language Functions.* Columbus, OH: Charles E. Merrill.

Stanovich, K. E. (1981). Relationships between word decoding speed, general name-retrieval ability, and reading progress in first-grade children. *Journal of Educational Psychology, 73,* 809–815.

Swastek, R. (1987). *Test-retest reliability concurrent validity study of the Experimental Test of Adolescent Word-Finding (E-TAWF).* Unpublished master's thesis, National College of Education, Evanston, IL.

Taylor-Sarno, M. T. (1981). *Acquired aphasia.* San Diego, CA: Academic Press.

Telser, E. (1971). *An assessment of word-finding skills in stuttering and non-stuttering children.* Unpublished doctoral dissertation, Northwestern University, Evanston, IL.

Telser, E., & Rutherford, D. (1970, November). *Word-finding abilities of stuttering and non-stuttering children.* Paper presented at the annual meeting of the American Speech and Hearing Association, New York.

Thorndike, E. L., & Lorge, I. (1944). *The teacher's word book of 30,000 words.* New York: Bureau of Publications, Teachers' College, Columbia University.

Tulving, E. (1974). Cue dependent forgetting. *American Scientist, 62,* 74–82.

Tulving, E., & Pearlstone, Z. (1966). Availability versus accessibility of information in memory for words. *Journal of Verbal Learning and Verbal Behavior, 5,* 381–391.

U.S. Bureau of the Census. (1980). *Educational attainment in the United States: March 1979 and 1978, Table 2* (Current Population Reports, Series P-20, No. 356). Washington, DC: USGPO.

Weisenburg, T., & McBride, K. E. (1964). *Aphasia: A clinical and psychological study.* New York: Hafner.

Wepman, J., Bock, D., Jones, L., & Van Pelt, D. (1956). Psycholinguistic study of aphasia: A revision of the concept of anomia. *Journal of Speech and Hearing Disorders, 21,* 468–476.

Weuffen, N. (1961). Testing of word-finding in normal and stuttering children. *Folia Phoniatrica, 13,* 267. (English summary)

Wiegel-Crump, C., & Dennis, M.D. (1986). Development of word-finding. *Brain and Language, 27,* 1–23.

Wiig, E. H., & Becker-Caplan, L. (1984). Linguistic retrieval strategies and word finding difficulties among children with language disabilities. *Topics in Language Disorders, 4*(3), 1–18.

Wiig, E. H., & Globus, D. (1971). Aphasic word identification as a function of logical relationship and association strength. *Journal of Speech and Hearing Research, 14,* 195–204.

Wiig, E. H., LaPointe, C., & Semel, E. M. (1977). Relationships among language processing and production abilities of learning disabled adolescents. *Journal of Learning Disabilities, 10,* 292–299.

Wiig, E., & Semel, E. M. (1975). Productive language abilities in learning disabled adolescents. *Journal of Learning Disabilities, 8,* 578–586.

Wiig, E. H., & Semel, E. M. (1976). *Language disabilities in children and adolescents.* Columbus, OH: Charles E. Merrill.

Wiig, E. H., & Semel, E. M. (1980). *Language assessment and intervention for the learning disabled.* Columbus, OH: Charles E. Merrill.

Wiig, E. H., & Semel, E. M. (1984). *Language assessment and intervention for the learning disabled* (rev. ed.). Columbus, OH: Charles E. Merrill.

Wiig, E. H., Semel, E. M., & Nystrom, L. A. (1982). Comparison of rapid naming abilities in language-learning-disabled and academically achieving eight-year-olds. *Language, Speech, and Hearing Services in Schools, 13,* 11–23.

Williams, S., & Canter, G. (1982). The influence of situational context on naming performance in aphasic syndromes. *Brain and Language, 17,* 92–106.

Wingfield, A. (1968). Effect of frequency on identification and naming of objects. *American Journal of Psychology, 81,* 226–234.

Wolf, M. (1980). The word-retrieval process and reading in children and aphasics. *Children's Language, 3,* 437–490.

Wolf, M., Bally, H., & Morris, R. (1984). *Automaticity, retrieval processes, and reading: A longitudinal study in average and impaired readers.* Unpublished manuscript.

Woodcock, R. W. (1973). *Woodcock Reading Mastery Tests.* Circle Pines, MN: American Guidance Service.

Wright, B. D., & Masters, G. N. (1982). *Rating scale analysis.* Chicago: Mesa Press.

Wright, B. D., & Stone, M. H. (1979). *Best test design.* Chicago: Mesa Press.

Yamadori, A., & Albert, M. (1973). Word category aphasia. *Cortex, 9,* 112–125.

APPENDIX A
Comprehension Scores for TAWF Items

A-1 Table A-1
Comprehension Scores
(percentage correct) for
TAWF Items for Adolescents
by Grade for Section 1,
Picture Naming: Nouns

Item	Seventh N 200	Eighth N 200	Ninth N 200	Tenth N 200	Eleventh N 200	Twelfth N 200
			Grades			
1	100.0	100.0	100.0	100.0	100.0	100.0
2	100.0	100.0	100.0	100.0	100.0	100.0
3	99.5	100.0	100.0	100.0	100.0	100.0
4	100.0	100.0	100.0	100.0	100.0	100.0
5	99.5	100.0	100.0	100.0	100.0	100.0
6	100.0	100.0	99.5	100.0	100.0	100.0
7	100.0	100.0	100.0	100.0	100.0	100.0
8	100.0	100.0	100.0	100.0	100.0	100.0
9	100.0	100.0	100.0	100.0	100.0	99.5
10	100.0	100.0	100.0	100.0	100.0	100.0
11	100.0	100.0	100.0	100.0	100.0	100.0
12	100.0	100.0	100.0	100.0	100.0	100.0
13	100.0	100.0	99.5	100.0	100.0	100.0
14	100.0	100.0	100.0	100.0	100.0	100.0
15	100.0	99.5	100.0	99.0	99.5	100.0
16	100.0	100.0	99.5	99.0	99.5	100.0
17	99.0	99.5	99.5	100.0	99.0	98.0
18	100.0	100.0	100.0	100.0	100.0	100.0
19	99.5	99.5	99.5	100.0	99.5	99.5
20	100.0	100.0	100.0	100.0	100.0	100.0
21	100.0	100.0	99.5	99.5	100.0	100.0
22	99.5	100.0	100.0	100.0	100.0	100.0
23	99.0	99.5	99.5	99.5	99.5	100.0
24	99.5	99.5	100.0	100.0	100.0	99.5
25	100.0	100.0	99.5	99.5	100.0	100.0
26	99.5	99.5	100.0	100.0	99.5	100.0
27	100.0	98.0	98.5	99.5	99.0	99.0
28	100.0	99.0	100.0	100.0	99.5	100.0
29	98.5	99.0	99.0	99.5	99.0	100.0
30	100.0	99.5	100.0	100.0	100.0	100.0
31	100.0	99.5	100.0	100.0	99.0	100.0
32	100.0	99.5	100.0	100.0	100.0	100.0
33	98.5	98.5	99.5	98.5	99.5	100.0
34	98.0	98.5	99.5	98.5	99.0	100.0
35	99.0	99.0	100.0	99.5	99.5	100.0
36	97.5	95.5	99.5	97.5	97.5	98.5
37	99.5	100.0	99.5	100.0	100.0	100.0

A-2 Table A-2

Comprehension Scores (percentage correct) for TAWF Items for Adolescents by Grade for Section 2, Sentence Completion Naming

Item	Grades					
	Seventh N 200	Eighth N 200	Ninth N 200	Tenth N 200	Eleventh N 200	Twelfth N 200
1	100.0	100.0	100.0	100.0	100.0	100.0
2	100.0	100.0	100.0	100.0	100.0	100.0
3	97.5	99.0	100.0	99.5	99.5	100.0
4	99.5	99.5	99.5	100.0	100.0	100.0
5	99.0	99.0	100.0	99.5	100.0	99.5
6	100.0	99.0	98.0	99.5	100.0	100.0
7	99.5	98.5	99.5	100.0	100.0	100.0
8	97.5	98.5	100.0	100.0	100.0	100.0
9	98.5	98.5	99.5	99.5	100.0	100.0
10	100.0	99.5	100.0	100.0	100.0	100.0
11	98.5	99.0	100.0	100.0	100.0	99.0
12	100.0	99.0	99.5	100.0	99.5	99.5
13	98.5	99.5	99.5	100.0	100.0	100.0
14	98.0	100.0	100.0	99.5	99.5	100.0
15	99.0	100.0	98.0	98.5	99.0	99.5
16	97.0	97.0	96.0	98.0	96.5	96.0

A-3 Table A-3

Comprehension Scores (percentage correct) for TAWF Items for Adolescents by Grade for Section 3, Description Naming

Item	Grades					
	Seventh N 200	Eighth N 200	Ninth N 200	Tenth N 200	Eleventh N 200	Twelfth N 200
1	100.0	100.0	100.0	100.0	99.5	100.0
2	100.0	100.0	100.0	100.0	100.0	100.0
3	99.5	100.0	99.5	100.0	100.0	100.0
4	100.0	99.0	100.0	100.0	99.5	100.0
5	97.0	99.5	100.0	100.0	100.0	99.5
6	99.5	100.0	100.0	100.0	100.0	100.0
7	99.0	100.0	99.0	100.0	99.5	100.0
8	98.5	99.0	99.5	99.0	100.0	100.0
9	99.0	96.5	96.0	97.5	97.0	98.0
10	98.5	98.5	99.5	100.0	98.5	100.0
11	98.5	96.0	97.0	99.0	98.0	98.5
12	98.0	97.0	98.5	99.0	98.5	99.0

A-4 Table A-4

Comprehension Scores (percentage correct) for TAWF Items for Adolescents by Grade for Section 4, Picture Naming: Verbs

	Grades					
Item	Seventh N 200	Eighth N 200	Ninth N 200	Tenth N 200	Eleventh N 200	Twelfth N 200
1	100.0	100.0	100.0	100.0	100.0	100.0
2	100.0	100.0	100.0	100.0	100.0	100.0
3	100.0	100.0	100.0	100.0	100.0	100.0
4	100.0	100.0	99.5	100.0	100.0	99.5
5	100.0	100.0	100.0	100.0	100.0	100.0
6	99.5	100.0	100.0	100.0	100.0	100.0
7	100.0	100.0	100.0	100.0	100.0	100.0
8	100.0	99.5	100.0	99.5	100.0	100.0
9	100.0	100.0	100.0	100.0	100.0	100.0
10	99.0	100.0	100.0	100.0	100.0	100.0
11	99.5	100.0	100.0	99.5	100.0	100.0
12	99.5	100.0	100.0	100.0	100.0	100.0
13	99.0	100.0	100.0	100.0	100.0	100.0
14	98.5	100.0	100.0	99.5	100.0	100.0
15	97.5	96.5	98.5	98.0	99.5	99.0
16	98.5	97.5	99.0	100.0	99.5	99.5
17	97.0	99.0	100.0	99.5	99.0	100.0
18	98.5	100.0	100.0	99.0	99.5	99.0
19	97.5	96.0	97.0	98.5	99.5	98.0
20	100.0	100.0	100.0	100.0	100.0	100.0
21	98.5	98.5	100.0	99.5	99.5	99.5

A-5 Table A-5

Comprehension Scores (percentage correct) for TAWF Items for Adolescents by Grade for Section 5, Category Naming

	Grades					
Item	Seventh N 200	Eighth N 200	Ninth N 200	Tenth N 200	Eleventh N 200	Twelfth N 200
1	100.0	100.0	100.0	100.0	100.0	100.0
2	97.5	99.0	99.5	99.0	99.5	99.5
3	99.5	100.0	100.0	100.0	100.0	100.0
4	100.0	100.0	100.0	100.0	100.0	100.0
5	100.0	99.5	100.0	99.5	100.0	100.0
6	100.0	100.0	100.0	98.0	100.0	100.0
7	99.5	100.0	100.0	100.0	100.0	100.0
8	97.0	100.0	99.5	100.0	100.0	100.0
9	99.0	100.0	100.0	99.5	100.0	100.0
10	99.5	99.5	100.0	100.0	99.5	100.0
11	99.5	100.0	99.0	100.0	100.0	100.0
12	100.0	100.0	100.0	100.0	100.0	100.0
13	98.0	96.5	98.5	99.0	99.5	99.5
14	100.0	98.0	99.0	100.0	100.0	100.0
15	99.0	98.5	96.5	97.0	98.5	100.0
16	99.5	100.0	100.0	100.0	100.0	100.0
17	100.0	99.5	100.0	100.0	99.5	99.5
18	99.5	99.5	99.5	100.0	100.0	99.5
19	99.0	100.0	98.0	99.5	99.5	100.0
20	100.0	99.5	100.0	100.0	100.0	100.0
21	94.5	98.0	99.0	97.0	98.0	96.5

A-6 Table A-6

Comprehension Scores (percentage correct) for TAWF Items for Adults by Age for Section 1, Picture Naming: Nouns

	Age		
Items	**20-0 to 39-11** ***N* 201**	**40-0 to 59-11** ***N* 200**	**60-0 to 80-0** ***N* 152**
1	100.0	100.0	100.0
2	100.0	99.0	100.0
3	100.0	100.0	100.0
4	100.0	100.0	100.0
5	100.0	100.0	100.0
6	100.0	100.0	100.0
7	100.0	100.0	99.3
8	100.0	100.0	100.0
9	100.0	100.0	100.0
10	100.0	99.5	100.0
11	100.0	100.0	100.0
12	100.0	99.5	100.0
13	100.0	100.0	100.0
14	100.0	100.0	98.6
15	100.0	98.5	97.3
16	100.0	100.0	98.0
17	100.0	99.0	100.0
18	100.0	99.5	100.0
19	100.0	99.5	100.0
20	100.0	100.0	99.3
21	100.0	100.0	100.0
22	100.0	98.0	96.0
23	100.0	100.0	99.3
24	100.0	100.0	99.3
25	100.0	99.0	100.0
26	100.0	100.0	100.0
27	100.0	100.0	100.0
28	100.0	100.0	99.3
29	100.0	100.0	100.0
30	100.0	100.0	100.0
31	100.0	100.0	100.0
32	100.0	100.0	98.0
33	99.5	98.0	98.6
34	100.0	100.0	98.6
35	100.0	100.0	98.0
36	99.0	100.0	98.6
37	99.0	99.5	98.0

A-7 Table A-7

Comprehension Scores (percentage correct) for TAWF Items for Adults by Age for Section 2, Sentence Completion Naming

Items	Age		
	20-0 to 39-11 *N* **201**	**40-0 to 59-11** *N* **200**	**60-0 to 80-0** *N* **152**
1	100.0	100.0	100.0
2	100.0	100.0	100.0
3	100.0	100.0	100.0
4	99.5	100.0	99.3
5	100.0	100.0	100.0
6	100.0	100.0	100.0
7	100.0	99.5	99.3
8	100.0	99.5	100.0
9	100.0	100.0	100.0
10	100.0	100.0	100.0
11	100.0	100.0	100.0
12	99.5	99.5	98.6
13	100.0	100.0	100.0
14	100.0	100.0	100.0
15	100.0	100.0	100.0
16	99.5	98.5	99.3

A-8 Table A-8

Comprehension Scores (percentage correct) for TAWF Items for Adults by Age for Section 3, Description Naming

Items	Age		
	20-0 to 39-11 *N* **201**	**40-0 to 59-11** *N* **200**	**60-0 to 80-0** *N* **152**
1	100.0	100.0	100.0
2	100.0	100.0	100.0
3	100.0	100.0	99.3
4	100.0	100.0	100.0
5	100.0	100.0	99.3
6	100.0	99.5	99.3
7	100.0	99.5	98.6
8	100.0	100.0	99.3
9	99.0	97.5	96.0
10	100.0	100.0	100.0
11	99.0	100.0	99.3
12	99.5	100.0	100.0

A-9 Table A-9

Comprehension Scores (percentage correct) for TAWF Items for Adults by Age for Section 4, Picture Naming: Verbs

Items	Age 20-0 to 39-11 N 201	40-0 to 59-11 N 200	60-0 to 80-0 N 152
1	100.0	100.0	100.0
2	100.0	100.0	100.0
3	100.0	100.0	99.3
4	100.0	100.0	100.0
5	100.0	100.0	100.0
6	100.0	100.0	100.0
7	100.0	100.0	100.0
8	100.0	100.0	100.0
9	100.0	100.0	100.0
10	100.0	100.0	99.3
11	100.0	100.0	100.0
12	100.0	100.0	100.0
13	100.0	100.0	100.0
14	100.0	100.0	100.0
15	100.0	99.5	99.3
16	99.5	99.5	99.3
17	100.0	100.0	100.0
18	100.0	100.0	100.0
19	99.0	98.5	98.0
20	100.0	100.0	100.0
21	100.0	99.5	100.0

A-10 Table A-10

Comprehension Scores (percentage correct) for TAWF Items for Adults by Age for Section 5, Category Naming

Items	Age 20-0 to 39-11 N 201	40-0 to 59-11 N 200	60-0 to 80-0 N 152
1	100.0	100.0	100.0
2	100.0	100.0	100.0
3	100.0	100.0	100.0
4	100.0	100.0	100.0
5	100.0	100.0	99.3
6	100.0	100.0	99.3
7	100.0	98.5	97.3
8	100.0	100.0	100.0
9	100.0	100.0	100.0
10	100.0	100.0	100.0
11	100.0	100.0	99.3
12	100.0	100.0	100.0
13	99.5	100.0	100.0
14	100.0	99.0	99.3
15	100.0	100.0	100.0
16	100.0	99.5	100.0
17	99.5	100.0	100.0
18	100.0	100.0	100.0
19	100.0	99.0	97.3
20	100.0	100.0	100.0
21	98.5	99.0	97.3